ELEMENTARY INTRODUCTION
TO
MOLECULAR SPECTRA

ELEMENTARY INTRODUCTION

TO

MOLECULAR SPECTRA

by

BØRGE BAK

SECOND, REVISED EDITION

1962

NORTH-HOLLAND PUBLISHING COMPANY

AMSTERDAM

PUBLISHERS:

NORTH-HOLLAND PUBLISHING CO., AMSTERDAM

SOLE DISTRIBUTORS FOR U.S.A.:
INTERSCIENCE PUBLISHERS, INC., NEW YORK

PRINTED IN THE NETHERLANDS

PREFACE TO THE FIRST EDITION

A steadily increasing number of biologists, chemists, and chemical engineers realize that their problems may now be most easily solved by spectroscopic methods. Since well-designed spectrographs appropriate for the simultaneous identification of several chemical components may now be acquired commercially, considerable success may now frequently be achieved by the non-spectroscopist on a purely empirical basis.

Sooner or later the desire for a somewhat broader understanding emerges, however, and experience has shown that existing monographs are not well suited for this purpose because of their volume. No single book treats the whole field of molecular spectra (microwave, infrared, and visible-ultraviolet spectra). In most monographs of this kind experimental spectroscopy has been entirely neglected.

In the present book it is intended to give a brief review of the principal types of molecular spectra. General features of spectrographs have been included in an introductory chapter in order that the reader should not be entirely ignorant of the experimental background.

It is hoped that the book, besides being of interest to the above-mentioned groups, will also prove to be useful to the student who contemplates a study of molecular spectroscopy and to scientists from other fields of science who wish to know how the results of molecular spectroscopy are obtained and can be applied.

In the second chapter a mathematical derivation of some important equations has been sketched. In order that this chapter may not prevent a study of the rest of the book it has been attempted to make the following chapters independent of chapter II.

Through references in the text the reader will find author names and the corresponding titles of the ponderous textbooks of molecular spectroscopy.

Copenhagen, Denmark   BØRGE BAK
December 1952

PREFACE TO THE SECOND EDITION

With the addition of a chapter on magnetic resonance spectra it is hoped that the book should serve its original purpose.

The author is indebted to Dr. William Dixon, Harvard, for valuable suggestions to improvements in orthography, vocabulary, and contents.

Copenhagen, Denmark   BØRGE BAK
February 1961

ACKNOWLEDGEMENTS

The author is greatly indebted to several of his colleagues who contributed essentially to this book or parts thereof. Professor Harald H. Nielsen, Ohio State University, Columbus, Ohio, U.S.A., professor Alex Langseth and Mr. Svend Brodersen, the Chemical Laboratory of the University of Copenhagen, Denmark, carefully went through the entire manuscript and made numerous valuable suggestions. Professor Christian Møller, the Institute of Theoretical Physics, Copenhagen, kindly read the second chapter.

For the assistance given to me in these and other ways I wish to express my best thanks.

BØRGE BAK
Chemical Laboratory of the University of Copenhagen

CONTENTS

CHAPTER I

INTRODUCTORY SURVEY OF PRACTICAL AND THEORETICAL SPECTROSCOPY

I. 1. UNITS AND SPECTRAL REGIONS

In earlier nomenclature a *spectroscope* was an instrument by which spectra could be observed directly by the eye. The science in which spectroscopes were applied was called *spectroscopy*. In our day the word spectroscopy covers studies of emission and absorption of all kinds of electromagnetic radiation. But since the role of the eye has been taken over by various detectors, such as the photographic plate, the photoelectric cell, etc., the word spectroscope has been replaced by the word *spectrograph*, referring to the fact that the instrument delivers some photographic or written record of the spectrum.

Electromagnetic radiation of wave-length λ and frequency ν obeys the relation

$$\lambda \times \nu = c,$$

where c is the velocity of the radiation. c is the same for electromagnetic radiation of all different 'kinds' (frequencies) and is, therefore, equal to the velocity of light, 2.99793×10^{10} cmsec^{-1}, *in empty space*. Radiation consisting of waves of only one frequency is said to be *monochromatic*. When monochromatic radiation passes from a vacuum to matter its velocity and wave-length are altered proportionally, the frequency being constant. By re-entrance of the radiation into a vacuum, λ and c return to their original values. When electromagnetic radiation is characterized by measuring its wave-length and not the frequency this circumstance must be taken into

1

account. If the source of radiation moves towards or away from the observer with great velocity a shift of frequency occurs (the *Doppler* effect). This is usually only of importance in astrophysics.

Electromagnetic radiation is known to exist throughout a wave-length range from about 10^{+6} to 10^{-12} cm. The inconvenience that would be caused if wave-lengths were always to be given in cm has been avoided by introducing units convenient for specific spectral 'regions'. Some of these units (the more commonly used) are given in table I.

TABLE I

SPECTRAL REGIONS AND UNITS

Spectral region	λ (cm)	Ordinarily applied unit	Spectral range	ν' (cm^{-1}
Microwave	$10-10^{-1}$	1 Mc sec^{-1} = 10^6 c sec^{-1}	3000–300 000 Mc sec^{-1}	0.1–10
Infrared	$10^{-1}-10^{-4}$	1 μ = 10^{-4} cm*	1000–1 μ	$10-10^4$
Visible-ultra-violet	$10^{-4}-10^{-5}$	1 Å = 10^{-8} cm	10 000–1000 Å	10^4-10^5

* 1 mμ = 10^{-3} μ

The unit ν', *the wave-number*, is defined as the reciprocal of λ_{vac} in cm. Hence,

$$\nu = \frac{c}{\lambda_{\text{vac}}} = \nu' \times c .$$

In this book frequencies will always be denoted by ν and wave-numbers by ν'. The wave-number of a spectral line is, however, often referred to as the 'frequency' of the line. As the wave-number is proportional to frequency it has the advantage (in common with e.g. Mc sec^{-1}) that it is proportional to the energy of the radiation quanta (compare below), and independent of the medium.

Electromagnetic radiation energy is quantized. The energy, E, of the single quantum is given by

$$E = h\nu = hc\nu'$$

where h is Planck's constant ($= 6.6252 \times 10^{-27}$ ergsec) and $hc = 1.9862 \times 10^{-16}$ ergcm. The energy of single and N radiation quanta, where N is Avogadro's number ($= 6.0232 \times 10^{23}$), throughout the spectral regions mentioned above are given in table II.

TABLE II

ENERGY OF SINGLE AND N RADIATION QUANTA
(N = AVOGADRO'S NUMBER)

Wave-numbers	10^{-1} cm^{-1}	10 cm^{-1}	10^4 cm^{-1}	10^5 cm^{-1}
g per single quantum	1.9862×10^{-17}	1.9862×10^{-15}	1.9862×10^{-12}	1.9862×10^{-11}
g per N quanta	1.1963×10^{7}	1.1963×10^{9}	1.1963×10^{12}	1.1963×10^{13}
cal per N quanta	2.8593×10^{-4}	2.8593×10^{-2}	2.8593×10^{1}	2.8593×10^{2}
es. electron-volt per single quantum	1.2398×10^{-5}	1.2398×10^{-3}	1.2398	1.2398×10^{1}

It has become common usage to give the energy of radiation quanta in cm^{-1} instead of ergs, i.e. to give the wave-number, $1/\lambda$, of the radiation instead of $h\nu$. Energy differences, given in cm^{-1}, are converted to ergs by multiplication by hc, as $(1/\lambda) \times hc = h\nu$.

Molecular spectroscopy deals mainly with absorption and emission of radiation in the spectral regions with a lower wave-length limit near 10^{-5} cm. The reason for this is readily seen. Chemical reactions by which molecules are formed or dissociated take place with a heat transfer to or from the surroundings of the order of magnitude from 0 to 200 kcal per mole. Irradiation of matter with radiation of wave-length shorter than 10^{-5} (i.e. $\nu' > 10^5$ cm^{-1}) will lead either to the dissociation of the molecule or to *scattering* of the radiation quantum (X-ray scattering).

It is hardly possible to give any *upper* limit to the wave-length of the radiation that will influence matter. Even the small quanta emitted by the most long-waved radio transmitters are undoubtedly absorbed by numerous types of molecules.

The division of the spectral range from 10 to 10^{-5} cm into the three spectral regions has a solid practical and theoretical background to be explained in succeeding sections.

I. 2. SPECTROSCOPIC EQUIPMENT

Although spectrographs – even those built to serve the same spectral region – may be constructed in such a variety of ways that they show little resemblance to each other in appearance and operation it is easy to identify certain elements that form part of all spectroscopic equipment, viz., the source of radiation, the sample container or cell, the monochromator, the detector and the detector output measuring unit. In microwave and magnetic resonance spectrographs the monochromator is superfluous but the general principle is the same as for other spectrographs.

Sources of Radiation

In *nuclear magnetic resonance* (NMR-) spectrographs the source of radiation is a crystal-controlled radio frequency oscillator operating in the 50 Mc sec^{-1} region.

Magnetrons and *klystrons* are sources of radiation in electron magnetic resonance (EMR-) equipment (3000–30 000 Mc sec^{-1}) and in microwave spectrographs (10 000–50 000 Mc sec^{-1}). The *klystron*, the more important of the two transmitters, is a specially developed electron tube in which the electrons on their way towards the 'plate' generate electromagnetic vibrations of suitable frequency (3000–300 000 Mc sec^{-1}) in a cavity. The klystron is rather unique as a radiation source as it gives off monochromatic and coherent radiation the frequency of which can be stabilized to 10^{-7} or better. By mechanical and electrical means the frequency may be altered only by about 10 per cent from an average value. Therefore, the experimenter needs a *set* of klystrons.

In the *infrared spectral region* the heat radiation from a *Nernst glower* or globar is usually applied from 1 to 25 μ. In the Nernst glower the filament consists of a mixture of oxides of e.g. cerium and thorium which are kept at high temperature ($\sim$ 1500°) electrically. The heat radiation is, of course, not monochromatic so that for use in spectrographs it must be followed by some dispersing element.

In the *visible-ultraviolet region* usual sources are *incandescent lamps* of many types or *discharge tubes,* such as the hydrogen discharge tube (giving off *continuous* radiation). No strictly monochromatic source is known. In 'Raman' spectrographs, where it is necessary that the source is almost monochromatic, the problem is solved by using a mercury arc in conjunction with a filter. The arc emits strong radiation in narrow regions around 2537, 3650, 4047, 4358, 5461 and 5780 Å. All emission other than, for example, the frequently applied 4358-radiation may then be removed by inserting a filter.

The Sample Container

Depending on its state of aggregation the sample is placed in a gas cell or a liquid cell. If a sufficiently large piece of crystalline material is available, it may be placed directly in the path of the radiation so that both reflected and traversing radiation may be analyzed. More frequently a thin film of the solid is produced on a transparent plate, or the finely powdered material is suspended in a transparent medium (for example, 'Nujol' or a potassium bromide plate).

The *'windows'* of the sample container must, of course, be transparent to the incident radiation. In the visible-ultraviolet region glass or quartz 'windows' are used. In the infrared region NaCl and KBr-windows are applied. If aqueous solutions are studied AgCl-windows are necessary. Microwave cells are closed with mica or plexiglass. Ordinary glass tubes suffice for NMR- and EMR-experiments.

The *wall material* and the windows must, of course, be chemically resistent to the sample. In microwave cells the walls play the unusual role of conducting high-frequency currents. They must, therefore, be made of material of good electrical conductivity.

The *linear dimensions* of gas cells are about 10 cm or more in length and a few centimeters in diameter. Owing to the greater molecular density of liquids and solids the length of the sample container in these cases may be as small as 0.01–0.1 mm.

A special problem arises in the microwave region where, for practical reasons, the cell dimensions can no longer be made large compared to the wavelength (~ 1 cm). If, for example, a cell of rectangular cross-section is used, the condition $2a > \lambda$ must be fulfilled, where a is the cross-sectional dimension perpendicular to the antenna through which the microwave energy is fed to the gas cell. If $\lambda > 2a$ no microwave energy can pass.

The Monochromator

Except in the case of microwave and magnetic resonance spectra some element is necessary by means of which the radiation can be separated in space according to wave-length after it has passed the sample. This part of the spectrograph is called the monochromator. Its principal part is a dispersing element, viz. a prism or a grating. The *prism* was the dispersing element first used in spectrographs. Transparency, dispersion and resolving power determine the choice of prism material used in different spectral regions.

Spectral region	Prism material
1200–2000 Å	CaF_2 or LiF
2000–4000 Å	Quartz
4000–20 000 Å (2 μ)	Glass
2–6 μ	LiF
5–15 μ	NaCl
15–25 μ	KBr
25–40 μ	TlBrI

Gratings can also be applied as dispersing elements in both the regions where prisms can be used and outside this region

(40–1000 μ). All the important features of the problem of prism spectrographs *versus* grating spectrographs have been very carefully discussed by Harrison, Lord, and Loofbourow*. Their book on practical spectroscopy presents a comprehensive discussion of many questions arising in connexion with practical spectroscopic work.

Until recently gratings were obtainable only in very limited numbers through a few scientific institutes, but the rapidly increasing demand for spectrographs has caused several industrial companies to produce very satisfactory gratings at prices which are no longer prohibitive.

The Detector

In all spectrographs the radiation that traverses the sample or is emitted by it must be analyzed with regard to radiation intensity as a function of wave-length. The radiation energy is measured by transforming it to some other form of energy, usually electrical energy. The 'transformer' is called the *detector*.

In the 50 Mc sec^{-1} region induction coils are used as detecting element. In the microwave region the detector is a *crystal rectifier*. At the higher frequencies in the infrared *thermopiles* are commonly used. The *eye*, the *photographic plate* and *photocells* are detectors for the visible region, the two last-mentioned being used also for the ultraviolet region. While the photographic plate was of dominating importance earlier it is now rapidly being replaced by photocells wherever possible.

The Detector Output Measuring Unit

In all cases of non-photographic detection a recording ammeter, oscilloscope or sometimes a compensation apparatus, operated by hand, is used as the instrument by which the detector output is measured. This unit usually includes an appropriate amplifier for the detector current.

* G. R. Harrison, R. C. Lord, J. R. Loofbourow, *Practical Spectroscopy* (Prentice Hall, Inc., New York, 1949).

I. 3. THE SPECTROGRAPH AND THE SPECTRUM

In the block diagram of fig. 1 the general set-up of a spectrograph for both emission and absorption experiments is shown.

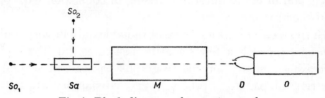

Fig. 1. Block diagram of a spectrograph.
So_1: Source of radiation at absorption experiments. Sa: Sample container. So_2: Source of radiation at emission experiments. M: Monochromator. D: Detector. O: Detector output measuring unit.

Irrespective of the way in which the detector output is given as a function of wave-length (wave-number) the result is called the *spectrum*. As no radiation source gives off radiation of constant intensity in more than very small intervals of wave-length and, furthermore, as the optical properties of

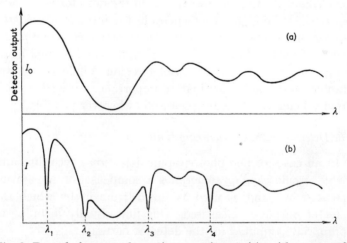

Fig. 2. Records from an absorption experiment. (a): with empty cell; (b): with sample in the cell. The sample absorbs radiation in regions around λ_1, λ_2, λ_3, and λ_4.

prisms and lenses vary with wave-length double experiments are necessary in the case of *absorption measurements* (fig. 2).

The *a*-curve is usually called the I_0-curve while the *b*-curve is called the *I*-curve. The result of an experiment is usually expressed by plotting the quantity *D*, the *optical density*, defined as $I = I_0 10^{-D}$ against the wave-length or wave-number. The underlying reason for this is given on p. 119–20 together with a definition of the so-called molar extinction coefficient.

In some cases *emission* of radiation from molecules may be investigated by placing vapours of the sample in a discharge tube. As a rule, however, only diatomic molecules can stand this treatment. Emission spectra of molecules may also be obtained from flames or from samples enclosed in a heated cell.

Magnetic resonance spectra are only observable when the sample is placed in a magnetic field. For experimental reasons the frequency of the source is here kept constant. The magnetic field intensity, *H*, is varied until resonance (absorption) occurs. Observed spectra are, therefore, often given as a function of *H* (to be discussed further in chapter VI).

I. 4. SPECTRA AND THEIR DEPENDENCE ON STATE OF AGGREGATION, PRESSURE AND TEMPERATURE

As a general result of molecular spectroscopy it has been found that molecular spectra are either continuous or discontinuous, so-called 'band' spectra.

In spectrographs with small resolving power the closely spaced lines of a band often appear unresolved, viz. as a real band.

Spectra of the same compound in the gaseous, liquid and solid state are usually different. First of all, much of the fine-structure that frequently is observed in the gas phase disappears, and only regions of continuous spectral activity (emission or absorption) occur. Fig. 3 is a typical example.

The effect has successfully been interpreted as due to the greater molecular density in the condensed phases. Secondly,

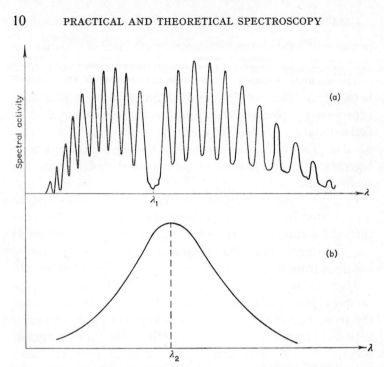

Fig. 3. Showing spectra of the same compound in (a) gaseous phase; (b) liquid phase; λ_1 and λ_2 may be equal or slightly different.

sometimes the absence of a band in the spectrum of a compound in a condensed phase corresponds to a band from the gaseous phase and vice versa. This may be interpreted as due to the formation of associates (polymers) in the condensed phase, the associates having a different spectrum, or, in the

TABLE III

EFFECT OF CHANGE OF PHASE ON SPECTRAL LINES OF CO_2 AND H_2S

Molecule	Gaseous state	Liquid state	Solid state
CO_2	1388.3 cm^{-1}	1387.5 cm^{-1}	1388 cm^{-1}
H_2S	2610.8 ,,	2573.6 ,,	$\begin{cases} 2546 \text{ ,,} \\ 2554 \text{ ,,} \\ 2521 \text{ ,,} \end{cases}$

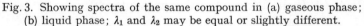

case of crystals, as due to lattice vibrations. To give an impression of the magnitude of the effect of phase-change, the absorption frequencies of CO_2 and H_2S in all three states of aggregation are compared in table III.

If the pressure of the gas is increased gradually (the temperature being kept constant), the single lines of the λ_1-band shown in fig. 3 are broadened. This effect has been accounted for as due to the increased number of molecular collisions. At pressures of from 50–100 atm the fine-structure may disappear so that the band will take on the appearance of fig. 4.

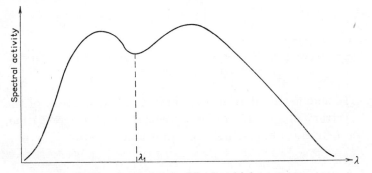

Fig. 4. Showing λ_1-band of fig. 3 at higher pressure.

It is nevertheless seen that a very pronounced difference exists between this intensity distribution and that for the condensed phase. If the pressure of a gas is kept constant, but the temperature changed, or if the temperature of a condensed phase is varied, the spectra observed at different temperatures may appear quite different. A typical example is shown in fig. 5.

Not only has the intensity distribution of the lines been substantially altered but new lines have appeared.

The effect may again be due to association or dissociation of the molecules but cases are also found where these phenomena can be excluded with certainty. The effect can then usually be accounted for by the changes in the distribution of molecules among the molecular energy levels (compare later).

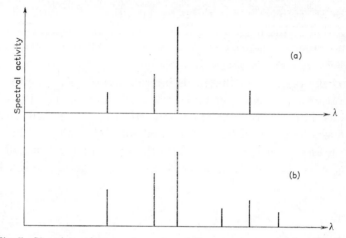

Fig. 5. Showing microwave spectra of the same compound at (a): low
temperature; (b): high temperature.

To summarize, it is of only limited value to speak of the 'spectrum' of a sample without giving its state of aggregation, the temperature, and the pressure simultaneously.

I. 5. MAIN RESULT OF MOLECULAR SPECTROSCOPY AND ITS INTERPRETATION

At a very early stage in the science of spectroscopy it was realized that the spectrum of a pure compound usually is a very valuable 'fingerprint' which successfully competes with the melting or boiling point, refractive index etc. as a means of identifying a substance. This 'fingerprint' property may to a large extent be used without a knowledge of how the spectrum is to be interpreted. Molecular spectra may, however, be given an interpretation in terms of molecular structure and dynamics which, at first sight, might seem to be of importance only to the theorist. It is necessary that the main features of this interpretation should be grasped also by the research worker who only wants to use the 'fingerprint' property.This knowledge will, for example, allow him to sort out in advance the existing cases of spectra that are *not* characteristic of a single molecular species.

As we shall see, band spectra are far more readily interpreted in detail than are continuous spectra. The fundamental equation that makes it possible to draw conclusions as to the mechanical properties of atoms and molecules when single discrete lines of frequency v occur is the frequency relation of *Niels Bohr*:

$$\Delta E = hv .$$

If radiation of frequency v is emitted or absorbed, the atom or molecule is capable of existence in two stationary states, separated by an energy difference ΔE.

We now use this equation to explain what might be called the *main result of experimental molecular spectroscopy*. For the sake of simplicity we shall here only refer to spectra of substances in field-free space, omitting magnetic resonance spectra.

Every pure compound – irrespective of its state of aggregation, pressure, and temperature – *shows strong spectral activity somewhere in the visible-ultraviolet region, somewhere in the infrared region and somewhere in the microwave region**.

Fig. 6. The total absorption spectrum of CH_3Cl (so far known) after D. K. Coles.

Fig. 6 is an illustration of this for CH_3Cl [from Donald K. Coles: Microwave Spectroscopy, Advances in Electronics II (Academic Press, Inc., New York, 1950)].

According to Bohr's equation molecular stationary states of three types must evidently exist: one type for which the separation of the energy levels is rather large (~ 100 kcal per mole or 35000 cm^{-1} per molecule), another type where the separation is about 1 kcal per mole or 350 cm^{-1} per mo-

---

* Molecules without a dipole moment form exceptions to this rule. The reason for this will be explained in chapters III, IV and V.

lecule and a third type where the separation is of the order of magnitude 0.01 kcal per mole or 3.5 cm^{-1} per molecule (compare table II, p. 3). Therefore, the molecules cannot obey the same mechanical laws – the Newtonian – as macroscopic bodies, for, if we thought of the molecule as being just a tiny tennis-ball, there would be no reason for its energy to assume only certain discrete values. Within certain limits, at least, the energy could be changed continuously. Spectroscopy, however, forces us to assume that the energy of atoms and molecules can only be changed in steps, quanta. Therefore, a mechanical theory differing from the Newtonian must be used, the *quantum mechanics*. In this chapter the interpretation of the spectra will be given by anticipating the results of quantum-mechanical calculations. A derivation of these equations will be sketched in the following chapter but it will be attempted to make the rest of the book fairly independent of chapter II.

The continuous energy changes of the tennis-ball are not contradictory to what takes place in molecules. The energy of a system consisting of a very large number of molecules may, of course, vary continuously although each member obeys the quantum rules.

The quantum-mechanical treatment of molecules in the gas-phase and in field-free space assumes that each molecule possesses translational, rotational, and vibrational energy like a macroscopic body but that the energy is quantized. The *energy diagram* shows the mutual positions of these *energy levels* (compare figs. 9 and 10). Radiation is *absorbed* if a molecule moves from a lower to a higher level and *emitted* in the reverse process. Our first task is to try to find out what kind of transitions are responsible for the spectral activity in the microwave region where quanta of approximate magnitude 10^{-16} erg per molecule (or 1 cm^{-1}) are exchanged (compare table II). One might first suspect changes in *translational* energy, E_{tr}, to be responsible. In the kinetic theory of gases it is calculated that $E_{\mathrm{tr}} = \frac{3}{2}kT$ per molecule where k is Boltzmann's constant $(= 1.38044 \times 10^{-16}$ erg per degree or 0.6950 cm^{-1}). At $T = 300°$K, $E_{tr} \sim 6 \times 10^{-14}$ erg, or about 200 cm^{-1}, an energy which is, indeed, far greater than the quanta exchanged in the microwave region. Might, therefore, these energy changes be interpreted as due to changes in translational energy?

A quantum-mechanical treatment of the problem gives the answer. If a *single* particle of mass m is let loose in an otherwise empty rectangular parallelepiped with edges a, b and c (the gas cell) its translational energy, E_{tr}, can, according to quantum theory, only take on the values given in (1):

$$E_{tr} = \frac{h^2}{8m} \left[\frac{n_x{}^2}{a^2} + \frac{n_y{}^2}{b^2} + \frac{n_z{}^2}{c^2} \right]. \tag{1}$$

As usual, h is Planck's constant. n_x, n_y, n_z are the so-called *quantum numbers*. The possible energy levels of translational energy are obtained by letting these numbers independently be *any integer*.

The *spacing* of these levels is very small. For every value of E_{tr} we can always let e.g. n_z be one and adjust n_x and n_y to an approximate reproduction of E_{tr}. But the levels adjacent to $(n_x, n_y, 1)$ are not farther removed than the $(n_x, n_y, 2)$-level, i.e. the spacing is certainly not greater than $3h^2/8mc^2$. Assuming $m = 100/(6.02 \times 10^{23})$ g and $c = 1$ cm we get that the spacing is approximately 10^{-32} erg per molecule or 10^{-16} cm^{-1}. Let us, furthermore, see what values n_x etc. must take on in order to reproduce E_{tr} at room temperature. Setting

$$\frac{h^2}{8m} \left[\frac{n_x{}^2}{a^2} + \frac{n_y{}^2}{b^2} + \frac{n_z{}^2}{c^2} \right] = 10^{-14} \text{ erg}$$

and letting $a = b = c = 1$ cm we find that the quantum on numbers must be of the order of magnitude 10^8.

Changes in translational energy that could account for the microwave spectra of gases would, therefore, have to take place from, for example, very small to very high quantum numbers. But very closely spaced around the levels involved there are other levels between which transitions might also take place. Thus, *continuous* spectral activity would result. Therefore, the strictly discontinuous spectrum of a gas in the microwave region cannot have its origin in changes in translational energy. If more molecules are admitted to the parallelepiped, collisions between molecules occur. It is convenient at this early stage to see how this influences (1) as well as our whole aspect of how well-defined all energy levels actually are.

The *Heisenberg uncertainty principle* will serve to throw light upon this problem. This principle states that the following relation exists between the period of time, Δt, in which the molecule is undisturbed and the uncertainty, ΔE, in the total energy E:

$$\Delta E \times \Delta t \geqslant h \,.$$

Δt may be taken as the average time between two collisions*. In a gas with n molecules per cm³ and a molecular diameter of σ cm each molecule of mass m collides approximately $n\sigma^2 \sqrt{(kT/m)}$ times per sec. We shall calculate this for three different cases: for a microwave experiment in which the pressure is 10^{-5} atm, for an experiment with an infrared spectrograph in which $p = 0.1$ atm and, finally, we shall bravely attempt to apply it to a liquid although the error in this case may, indeed, be large. Setting $\sigma = 3$ Å, $T = 300°$K and $m = 100/(6.02 \times 10^{23})$ g we get:

	Numb. of collisions sec⁻¹	Δt (sec)	ΔE (erg)	ΔE (cm⁻¹)
Gas at 10^{-5} atm	2×10^3	0.5×10^{-3}	13×10^{-24}	6×10^{-8}
Gas at 10^{-1} atm	2×10^7	0.5×10^{-7}	13×10^{-20}	6×10^{-4}
Liquid (molar vol. 100 cm³)	6×10^{10}	1.7×10^{-11}	3.8×10^{-16}	2

This indeterminacy is, as we see, more than sufficient to 'blur' completely the system of discrete translational energy levels

---

* Strictly spoken between two perturbations of any kind.

(1), the spacing of which is about 10^{-16} cm^{-1} per molecule. As we are always dealing with a very large number of molecules in a spectroscopic experiment we see that for such a system the concept of discrete translational energy levels breaks down.

It is, however, satisfying to note that this indeterminacy of energy is vanishingly small for *gases* compared to the quanta which we find that they absorb or emit in the microwave, infrared, and visible-ultraviolet regions. For *liquids*, a possible effect of this kind is obscured by equally great effects because of electrical interaction between the molecules. This means that the levels with the smallest spacing (~ 0.01 kcal per mole or about 1 cm^{-1} per molecule) are also 'blurred'.

We now turn to a calculation of the *rotational energy*, E_{rot}, of molecules. Quantum mechanics teaches that E_{rot} for a linear molecule in the gas phase obeys the relation

$$E_{\text{rot}} = \frac{h^2}{8\pi^2 I} J(J+1) \qquad (2)$$

where I is the moment of inertia ($= \Sigma\, m_i r_i^2$, m_i being the mass of the ith atom and r_i its distance from the centre of mass). J is the *rotational quantum number* which is always an integer, including 0. If we assume that the interatomic distances in molecules are the same in the gas phase as in the crystalline state where they can be estimated from a knowledge of the density (or, found exactly by X-ray scattering), I must be of the order of magnitude 10^{-38} gcm^2. The change in E_{rot} by, for example, the transition $J = 1 \to 2$, therefore, becomes $(h^2/8\pi^2 I)(6-2) = h^2/2\pi^2 I$. Using Bohr's frequency rule we have

$$h\nu_{\text{abs}} = \frac{h^2}{2\pi^2 I} \quad \text{or} \quad \lambda_{\text{abs}} = \frac{2\pi^2 c I}{h}$$

which is about one cm.

Molecules generally have three different 'principal' moments of inertia (chapter III) but a similar result is found in all cases. Thus, *spectral activity in field-free space in the microwave region can be interpreted as due to changes in molecular rotational energy.*

The spectral activity in the *'prism infrared'* (2–25 μ) is due to the elastic properties of the molecules. Considering a diatomic molecule we may think of it as having an interior potential energy, V, depending on the interatomic distance, r, as shown in fig. 7.

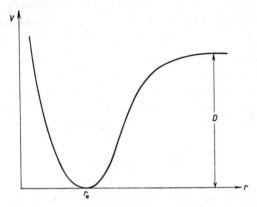

Fig. 7. General shape of potential curve for diatomic molecule. r_e = interatomic distance in equilibrium position. D = dissociation energy.

At every distance the restoring force, the *valence force,* equals $-\partial V/\partial r$. Near the equilibrium position this force is approximately $-k(r-r_e)$ which is *Hooke's law* (known from the mechanical treatment of macroscopic bodies). k is called the *force-constant*, D is the *dissociation energy*. We know the approximate value of D from chemical reactions but this is, of course, insufficient to define the valence force, $-\partial V/\partial r$. This quantity we must know if we want to make it plausible that the infrared spectral activity is due to changes in the 'elastic' energy V. In the derivation of (2) p. 17 it is assumed that the molecule is rigid, so that its linear dimensions are conserved for all rotational quantum numbers. This, of course, cannot be strictly true as all rotating bodies are subject to centrifugal stretching. The approximation (2) is nevertheless very good and reproduces microwave spectra to a high degree of accuracy. If on the other hand it is assumed that the necessary centripetal force for $J \geqslant 1$ is provided by the valence force, the following formula can be derived:

$$E_{rot} = \frac{h^2}{8\pi^2 I} J(J+1) - \frac{h^4}{32\pi^4 I^2 r_e^2 k} J^2(J+1)^2 .$$

In a few instances, for example HCl, it has been possible to measure this small effect. It was found that a k-value near 5×10^5 dynes cm^{-1} must be used in order to reproduce the experimental data.

We are now able to predict where changes in quantized elastic energy are to be sought by a spectrograph. The quantum-mechanical calculation for a diatomic molecule in the gas phase shows that the elastic energy, or, as it is usually called, the *vibrational energy*, E_{vib}, is given by

$$E_{vib} = \frac{h}{2\pi} \sqrt{k \frac{m_1 + m_2}{m_1 m_2}} (n + \tfrac{1}{2}) . \tag{3}$$

m_1 and m_2 are the masses of the atoms involved. $m_1 m_2 / (m_1 + m_2)$ is often called the 'reduced' mass of the molecule and written as μ. n is the *vibrational quantum number* which can take on the values 0, 1, 2, 3 ... . While E_{rot} may become zero for $J = 0$, $n = 0$ gives $E_{vib} = (h/4\pi)\sqrt{(k/\mu)}$, the *zero-point energy*.

The energy change, ΔE_{vib}, for the absorption process $n = 0 \to 1$ is

$$\Delta E_{vib} = \frac{h}{2\pi} \sqrt{\frac{k}{\mu}} .$$

If we apply Bohr's frequency rule we get

$$h\nu_{abs} = \frac{h}{2\pi} \sqrt{\frac{k}{\mu}} \quad \text{or} \quad \lambda_{abs} = 2\pi c \sqrt{\frac{\mu}{k}} .$$

For $\mu = 1.6 \times 10^{-24}$ g and $k = 5 \times 10^5$ dynes/cm one calculates $\lambda_{abs} = 3.3\ \mu$ or $\nu'_{abs} = 3000$ cm^{-1}. Therefore, the strong infrared absorption band of HCl in the gas phase at 2885 cm^{-1} may safely be interpreted as due to a change in the vibrational energy of the molecule.

Let us also carry through a classical-mechanical calculation of the vibrational frequency ν_m of the HCl-molecule.

$$-\frac{\partial V}{\partial r} = -k(r - r_e) = \mu \frac{\partial^2 r}{\partial t^2} = \mu \frac{\partial^2 (r - r_e)}{\partial t^2}.$$

Setting $r - r_e$ equal to x we can write

$$kx = -\mu \frac{\partial^2 x}{\partial t^2}.$$

This differential equation has the solution

$$x = A \sin 2\pi\nu_m t.$$

The mechanical vibrational frequency, ν_m, can be found by insertion. As

$$\frac{\partial^2 x}{\partial t^2} = -4\pi^2 \nu_m{}^2 A \sin 2\pi\nu_m t$$

we get

$$\nu_m = \frac{1}{2\pi} \sqrt{\frac{k}{\mu}} = \nu_{abs}.$$

Hence, the frequency of absorbed or emitted radiation as found by quantum mechanics is identical with ν_m. The absorption frequencies found in the infrared region are, therefore, often called the vibrational frequencies of the molecule.

If the molecule consists of more than two atoms it is capable of carrying out an infinite number of different vibrations about its equilibrium position. But it can be shown that every vibration can be thought of as formed by suitable superposition of $3N - 6$ so-called *normal vibrations*, N being the number of atoms in the molecule. Simultaneously it can be shown that the molecule will show strong infrared absorption at $3N - 6$ different frequencies*. These important normal vibrations are

* On the so-called 'selection rules' limiting this statement see later (page 51).

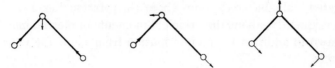

Fig. 8. Showing normal vibrations of triatomic molecule.

generally pictured as shown in fig. 8 for a triatomic molecule.

Compared to the microwave spectrum the infrared spectrum is considerably more complicated because not only do transitions occur between the vibrational levels but the much smaller rotational energy quanta are also exchanged during absorption and emission processes. Instead of the above-mentioned $3N-6$ single frequencies one normally gets $3N-6$ more or less complicated infrared *bands*. Fig. 9 shows how the

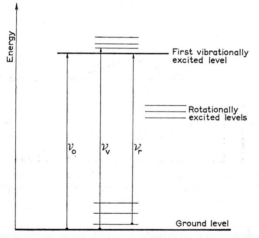

Fig. 9. Showing vibrational and rotational energy levels and how so-called rotational fine-structure components (ν_v and ν_r) are to be expected beside the line for pure vibrational transition (ν_0).

spectral line corresponding to the pure vibrational transition (ν_0) is surrounded by a number of other lines, such as ν_v and ν_r.

If such a band can be resolved (which may be done by means of a spectrograph of high resolving power) and interpreted, valuable conclusions about the rotational energy and, consequently, about the principal moments of inertia, may be drawn in addition to the information from ν_0 on the valence forces.

The *visible-ultraviolet region*, the 'classical' domain of spectroscopy, is the region in which a great number of *atomic* emission

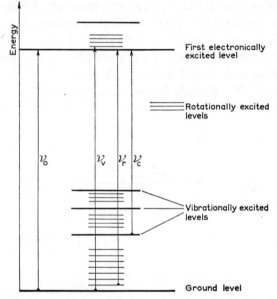

Fig. 10. Showing rotational fine-structure components (ν_v and ν_r) around pure electronic transition (ν_0) and coarse-structure component ν_c.

spectra have been studied. As will be known, the spectral activity of atoms is explained by assuming that the electrons may only occupy certain 'orbits' around the nucleus. If an electron 'jumps' from an orbit that corresponds to a large distance from the nucleus to another, representing a smaller distance, radiation is emitted.

Obviously, the molecular spectra in the visible-ultraviolet can be interpreted in much the same way. Molecular spectra in this region are, of course, far more complicated than atomic spectra, even far more complicated than microwave and infrared spectra. The explanation for this complexity is that the great changes in electronic energy are usually accompanied by exchange of the much smaller vibrational and rotational quanta. Fig. 10 shows how the 'backbone' of a visible-ultraviolet absorption spectrum arises.

The drawing refers, of course, to the gas state and not to liquids or solutions where it is almost out of question to speak of rotational levels. However, experience has shown that spectra observed in this spectral region on even rather dilute gases frequently are diffuse or continuous. This phenomenon, which is unparalleled in infrared and microwave spectroscopy, will be dealt with in chapter v. It is due to the circumstance that the radiation quanta of this spectral region are comparable in magnitude to the dissociation energy of molecules.

CHAPTER II

DERIVATION OF SOME IMPORTANT
EQUATIONS IN SPECTROSCOPY †

II. 1. INTRODUCTION

Quantum mechanics certainly has led to an understanding in principle of most problems in chemistry and physics, but in very many cases the route from the fundamental postulates to the problem in question is quite difficult to follow. This is not true in the case of spectroscopy. Indeed the spectroscopic phenomena belong to those which are most readily accounted for by quantum mechanics. This, of course, is due to a large extent to the fact that it was the experimental results of spectroscopy which forced quantum mechanics to be created. It is, therefore, highly desirable that the student of spectroscopy should grasp something of the quantum mechanical calculations that lead to formulae like (1), (2) and (3) from the preceding chapter. Indeed, a combined study of elementary spectroscopy and quantum mechanics seems to be of high value for a further penetration into either of the two subjects.

Only little space can be devoted in this book to mathematical deductions. Readers interested in quantum mechanics itself are referred to *Rojansky*'s book* 'Introductory Quantum Mechanics' or to 'Introduction to Quantum Mechanics', the book by *Pauling* and *Wilson*. Later treatments by *Kramers* and by *Schiff* may likewise be recommended.**

† Readers not interested in this topic may proceed to chapter III.
* V. Rojansky, *Introductory Quantum Mechanics* (Prentice-Hall, New York, 1946).
** L. Pauling and E. Bright Wilson, *Introduction to Quantum Mechanics* (McGraw-Hill, New York and London, 1935). H. A. Kramers, *Quantum*

24

It will be attempted here to give briefly the manner in which the so-called *Schrödinger* equation appropriate to the various problems can be deduced. No detailed mathematical procedures for solving these equations will be given but it will be attempted to clarify how the quantization of energy, 'space' quantization, selection rules etc., emerge.

II. 2. OPERATORS, OPERANDS, EIGENFUNCTIONS, AND EIGENVALUES

Operators are means of indicating mathematical operations. The operators d/dx and c, for example, indicate differentiation with respect to x and multiplication by the constant c. The function that is going to be differentiated, multiplied etc., is called the *operand*.

Any operator may, of course, operate on any function. If the result of the operation is sufficiently simple so that it may be written as the function (operand) itself multiplied by a constant the operand is said to be an *eigenfunction* of the operator in question. The constant is called the *eigenvalue*.

Thus, $\exp kx$ is an eigenfunction of the operator d/dx as $(d/dx) \exp kx = k \times \exp kx$. Here, k is the eigenvalue.

In quantum mechanics a very important class of eigenfunctions, sometimes called the *well-behaved* eigenfunctions, are of particular interest. Among all possible eigenfunctions of a given operator they are chosen so as to be single-valued and to remain finite without being identically zero for all values of the independent variables. The functions and their derivatives must be continuous. Clearly, these conditions point towards assigning a physical meaning to the eigenfunctions in one way or another. $\exp kx$ in the example above is *not* a well-behaved function so that the operator d/dx has *no* well-behaved eigenfunction. The operator $-i(d/dx)$, on the other hand, does have well-behaved eigenfunctions since $-i(d/dx)f(x) = k \times f(x)$ has the solution $f(x) = \exp ikx = \cos kx + i \sin kx$. This function satisfies all the conditions above.

II. 3. THE HAMILTONIAN OPERATOR AND THE WAVE-FUNCTIONS

In classical mechanics the equations of motion of a system are often given in the so-called Hamiltonian form. The classical 'Hamiltonian' expresses that the total energy, E, of a conservative system equals the sum of its kinetic energy (T) and the potential energy (V). T may be written as $T = \frac{1}{2}\Sigma m_i$ $(\dot{x}_i^2 + \dot{y}_i^2 + \dot{z}_i^2)$, where $(\dot{x}_i, \dot{y}_i, \dot{z}_i)$ are the components of the velocity of the ith particle of mass m_i.

Introducing

$$p_{x_i} = m_i \dot{x}_i, \qquad p_{y_i} = m_i \dot{y}_i, \qquad p_{z_i} = m_i \dot{z}_i$$

we can write E in the Hamiltonian form where one usually writes H instead of E:

$$H = \frac{1}{2}\Sigma \frac{1}{m_i}(p_{x_i}^2 + p_{y_i}^2 + p_{z_i}^2) + V(x_i, y_i, z_i) .$$

If the procedure indicated below is followed the right-hand side of this expression becomes an operator, the *Hamiltonian operator*.

I. All coordinates and functions of coordinates (x^2, $r = \sqrt{(x^2 + y^2 + z^2)}$ etc., but *not* time derivatives) are left unchanged, being simply multipliers. So are the constants.

II. Momenta are substituted according to the rules

$$p_x \rightarrow \frac{h}{2\pi i}\frac{\partial}{\partial x}, \qquad p_y \rightarrow \frac{h}{2\pi i}\frac{\partial}{\partial y}, \qquad p_z \rightarrow \frac{h}{2\pi i}\frac{\partial}{\partial z} .$$

p_x^2 is interpreted as meaning operation with $(h/2\pi i)\partial/\partial x$ twice, i.e. $p_x^2 \rightarrow -(h^2/4\pi^2)\partial^2/\partial x^2$.

For example, the Hamiltonian operator for the hydrogen

atom is*

$$\mathscr{H} = \frac{-h^2}{8\pi^2 m}\left(\frac{\partial^2}{\partial x^2} + \frac{\partial^2}{\partial y^2} + \frac{\partial^2}{\partial z^2}\right) - \frac{e^2}{r}.$$

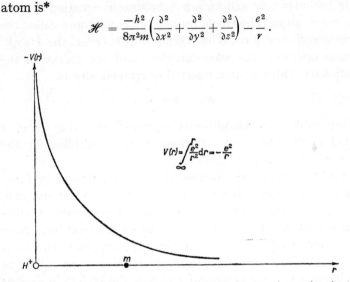

$$V(r) = \int_{\infty}^{r} \frac{e^2}{r^2} dr = -\frac{e^2}{r}$$

Fig. 11. Potential energy, $V(r)$, of electron (mass m) moving in the field of the proton (H+).

The fundamental postulate which we are going to use in the following is:

The well-behaved eigenfunctions of the Hamiltonian operator are the so-called wave-functions. The corresponding eigenvalues are the energies of the stationary states.

Hence, in the case of hydrogen, we have

$$-\frac{h^2}{8\pi^2 m}\left(\frac{\partial^2\psi}{\partial x^2} + \frac{\partial^2\psi}{\partial y_2} + \frac{\partial^2\psi}{\partial z^2}\right) - \frac{e^2}{r}\psi = E \times \psi.$$

The functions ψ satisfying the equation are the wave-functions and the constants E are the energy values of the stationary states. Written in the form

$$\frac{\partial^2\psi}{\partial x^2} + \frac{\partial^2\psi}{\partial y^2} + \frac{\partial^2\psi}{\partial z^2} + \frac{8\pi^2 m}{h^2}\left(\frac{e^2}{r} + E\right)\psi = 0$$

* Because of its great mass and small velocity the contribution from the nucleus has been ignored. The electronic mass is called m.

this becomes the well-known Schrödinger equation for the hydrogen atom. The whole procedure is sometimes called the *Schrödinger procedure*. The relationship between the Hamiltonian operator, the wave-functions and the energy of the stationary states is often referred to symbolically as

$$\mathscr{H}\psi = E \times \psi$$

which reads: The Hamiltonian operator, operating on ψ, is equal to the energy of a stationary state multiplied by the corresponding wave-function.

The wave-functions themselves often are imaginary functions without any direct physical meaning. Their use can, however, be generally justified because considerable mathematical labour is saved compared to what would have been necessary if only real functions had been applied. The function $\psi\psi^*$ [†] which is real can be interpreted as meaning the probability density function for finding the system in various configurations, e.g. for finding the electron at a certain distance from the proton. This requires that the condition

$$\int_\sigma \psi\psi^* \mathrm{d}\tau = 1$$

must be fulfilled[††] and it is therefore usually necessary to multiply the wave-functions with suitable constants. Wave-functions obeying the condition above are said to be *normalized*.

II. 4. THE PARTICLE IN A BOX

We shall deduce (1), page 15, by means of the Schrödinger technique. Fig. 12 shows the coordinate system, the dimensions of the rectangular parallelepiped etc.

The Hamiltonian is

$$H = \frac{1}{2m}\,(p_x{}^2 + p_y{}^2 + p_z{}^2) + V\,.$$

[†] ψ^* is complex conjugated to ψ.
[††] σ means integration over the whole space.

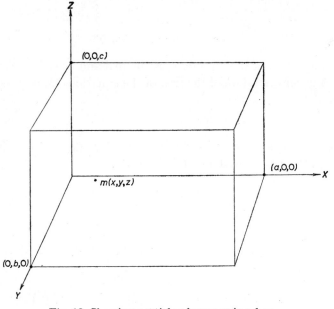

Fig. 12. Showing particle of mass m in a box.

The equation $\mathscr{H}\psi = E \times \psi$, therefore, becomes:

$$-\frac{h^2}{8\pi^2 m}\left(\frac{\partial^2\psi}{\partial x^2} + \frac{\partial^2\psi}{\partial y^2} + \frac{\partial^2\psi}{\partial z^2}\right) + V\psi = E\psi. \tag{1}$$

Inside the box V is of course zero. For $V = 0$ let us try to write $\psi(x, y, z)$ as a product of three functions, each function depending only on the suffix coordinate:

$$\psi(x, y, z) = \psi_x \times \psi_y \times \psi_z. \tag{2}$$

If we introduce (2) into (1) and divide through by $\psi_x\psi_y\psi_z$ we get

$$\frac{\partial^2\psi_x}{\partial x^2}\frac{1}{\psi_x} + \frac{\partial^2\psi_y}{\partial y^2}\frac{1}{\psi_y} + \frac{\partial^2\psi_z}{\partial z^2}\frac{1}{\psi_z} + \frac{8\pi^2 mE}{h^2} = 0.$$

x, y and z are independent variables. If we fix two of them the third may still vary unrestrictedly. But this must mean that

$$\frac{\partial^2 \psi_x}{\partial x^2}\frac{1}{\psi_x} = c_x , \qquad \frac{\partial^2 \psi_y}{\partial y^2}\frac{1}{\psi_y} = c_y , \qquad \frac{\partial^2 \psi_z}{\partial z^2}\frac{1}{\psi_z} = c_z , \qquad (3)$$

$$c_x + c_y + c_z = -8\pi^2 mE/h^2 \qquad (4)$$

where the constants c_x, etc. must be real and negative.

A general solution of the first of the equations (3) is:

$$\psi_x = A_x e^{i\sqrt{(-c_x)}x} + B_x e^{-i\sqrt{(-c_x)}x} .$$

The presence of the walls of the box is now taken into account by putting $\psi_x = 0$ at $x = 0$ and $x = a$.

$$A_x + B_x = 0$$

$$A_x(e^{i\sqrt{(-c_x)}a} - e^{-i\sqrt{(-c_x)}a}) = 2iA_x \sin \sqrt{(-c_x)}a = 0 .$$

The last equation can only be satisfied if $a\sqrt{(-c_x)} = n_x \pi$, where $n_x = 0, \pm 1, \pm 2,....$. Therefore,

$$c_x = -n_x^2 \left(\frac{\pi}{a}\right)^2 \qquad c_y = -n_y^2 \left(\frac{\pi}{b}\right)^2 \qquad c_z = -n_z^2 \left(\frac{\pi}{c}\right)^2$$

which, combined with (4), gives for the energies

$$E = \frac{h^2}{8m}\left[\left(\frac{n_x}{a}\right)^2 + \left(\frac{n_y}{b}\right)^2 + \left(\frac{n_z}{c}\right)^2\right] . \qquad (5)$$

This is (1), page 15. The wave-functions are:

$$\psi(x, y, z) = -8iA_xA_yA_z [\sin \sqrt{(-c_x)}x] [\sin \sqrt{(-c_y)}y] [\sin \sqrt{(-c_z)}z] .$$

If we want to *normalize* $\psi(x,y,z)$ the constant

$$64 A_x A_x^* A_y A_y^* A_z A_z^*$$

which is real, enters. Calling the constant K we get:

$$K \int_0^a \int_0^b \int_0^c [\sin^2 \sqrt{(-c_x)}x] [\sin^2 \sqrt{(-c_y)}y] [\sin^2 \sqrt{(-c_z)}z] \, dx dy dz = 1$$

giving $K = 8/abc$ or:

$$\psi(x, y, z) = \sqrt{\frac{8}{abc}} \left[\sin n_x \frac{\pi}{a} x\right]\left[\sin n_y \frac{\pi}{b} y\right]\left[\sin n_z \frac{\pi}{c} z\right]. \qquad (6)$$

In (6), n_x etc. may not become zero in which case $\psi(x,y,z)$ would be 0 throughout the box.

There is no need for discussing the eigenvalues (5) further. As shown on page 15 the spacing of the energy levels of the single particle is so small that the uncertainty of the energy which grows bigger and bigger when more and more molecules are admitted to the box widely overshadows the 'ideal' spacing at even the smallest experimental pressures.

The wave-functions and the probability density functions take the form of 'waves'. If, for example, we examine the functions $\psi(x, y, z)$ and $\psi^2(x, y, z)$ along the line $y = \frac{1}{2}b$, $z = \frac{1}{2}c$ for the case $(n_x, n_y, n_z) = (2, 1, 1)$ we get

$$\psi(x, y, z) = \sqrt{\frac{8}{abc}} \sin \frac{2\pi}{a} x \qquad \text{and} \qquad \psi^2(x, y, z) = \frac{8}{abc} \sin^2 \frac{2\pi}{a} x.$$

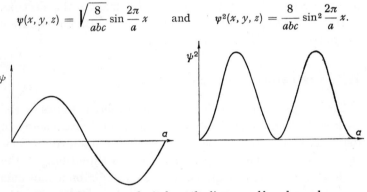

Fig. 13. Shows ψ and ψ^2 along the line $y = \frac{1}{2}b$ and $z = \frac{1}{2}c$.

We may, therefore, associate a wave-length λ_a with the motion of the particle in the x-direction. If we choose the ψ-curve we must put $\lambda_a = a$. We will examine how this 'wave' description is related to the classical 'particle' description of the molecule as moving with velocity v_x in the x-direction. $(n_x, n_y, n_z) = (2, 1, 1)$ corresponds to

$$E = \frac{h^2}{8m}\left(\frac{4}{a^2} + \frac{1}{b^2} + \frac{1}{c^2}\right)$$

which classically must be interpreted as the kinetic energy $\frac{1}{2}mv_x^2 + \frac{1}{2}mv_y^2 + \frac{1}{2}mv_z^2$. Therefore,

$$\tfrac{1}{2}mv_x^2 = \frac{h^2}{2ma^2} \, .$$

But since $\lambda_a = a$ we get

$$\lambda_a = \frac{h}{mv_x} \, .$$

This is the famous *de Broglie* relation between particle momentum (mass $\times$ velocity) and the associated wave-length λ_a. The equation has been confirmed by the important experiment by *Davisson and Germer* [Phys. Rev. *30*, 705 (1927)] in which a beam of electrons of uniform velocity v_e showed diffraction phenomena when passing a metal foil as if X-rays of wave-length h/mv_e had been used, m being the mass of the electron.

It is interesting to note that the λ_a of the de Broglie equation refers to the ψ and *not* to the ψ^2-function.

II. 5. THE TWO-BODY PROBLEM

Under this heading such apparently different topics as the hydrogen atom and the vibrational and rotational energy of diatomic molecules can be treated by a common mathematical procedure. This is, perhaps, not too astonishing if the hydrogen atom is considered as the simplest diatomic molecule in nature with a valence force identical with the Coulomb attraction. Of course, for diatomic molecules the force law is different, so that a separate treatment of the hydrogen atom and the diatomic molecule is necessary as soon as the force law has to be specified.

Until further notice we may just think of the atom and the molecule as having some kind of internal potential, $V(r)$. Then the Hamiltonian is:

$$H = \frac{1}{2m_1}(p_{x_1}^2 + p_{y_1}^2 + p_{z_1}^2) + \frac{1}{2m_2}(p_{x_2}^2 + p_{y_2}^2 + p_{z_2}^2) + V(r) \, .$$

The Hamiltonian operator is:

$$\mathscr{H} = \frac{-h^2}{8\pi^2 m_1}\left(\frac{\partial^2}{\partial x_1{}^2} + \frac{\partial^2}{\partial y_1{}^2} + \frac{\partial^2}{\partial z_1{}^2}\right) - \frac{h^2}{8\pi^2 m_2}\left(\frac{\partial^2}{\partial x_2{}^2} + \frac{\partial^2}{\partial y_2{}^2} + \frac{\partial^2}{\partial z_2{}^2}\right) + V(r) \; .$$

The Schrödinger equation becomes:

$$\frac{-h^2}{8\pi^2 m_1}\left(\frac{\partial^2\psi}{\partial x_1{}^2} + \frac{\partial^2\psi}{\partial y_1{}^2} + \frac{\partial^2\psi}{\partial z_1{}^2}\right) - \frac{h^2}{8\pi^2 m_2}\left(\frac{\partial^2\psi}{\partial x_2{}^2} + \frac{\partial^2\psi}{\partial y_2{}^2} + \frac{\partial^2\psi}{\partial z_2{}^2}\right) + V(r)\psi = E\psi$$

or

$$\frac{1}{m_1}\left(\frac{\partial^2\psi}{\partial x_1{}^2} + \frac{\partial^2\psi}{\partial y_1{}^2} + \frac{\partial^2\psi}{\partial z_1{}^2}\right) + \frac{1}{m_2}\left(\frac{\partial^2\psi}{\partial x_2{}^2} + \frac{\partial^2\psi}{\partial y_2{}^2} + \frac{\partial^2\psi}{\partial z_2{}^2}\right) + \frac{8\pi^2}{h^2}(E - V(r))\psi = 0. \tag{1}$$

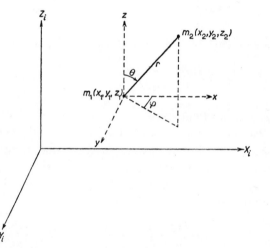

Fig. 14. Showing coordinate system fixed in space (X_i, Y_i, Z_i), coordinate system following the molecule (x, y, z), and polar system (r, θ, φ).

The 'molecule' is capable of carrying out a translational motion while simultaneously the distance between the two particles may change and the whole molecule may rotate. The coordinates x_1, y_1, z_1, x_2, y_2, z_2, are not well suited to distinguish between these possibilities. First, the coordinates of the center of mass, (X, Y, Z), are introduced:

$$X = \frac{1}{M}(m_1 x_1 + m_2 x_2), \qquad Y = \frac{1}{M}(m_1 y_1 + m_2 y_2),$$

$$Z = \frac{1}{M}(m_1 z_1 + m_2 z_2), \qquad M = m_1 + m_2.$$

If, in addition, we introduce

$$x = x_2 - x_1, \qquad y = y_2 - y_1, \qquad z = z_2 - z_1,$$

the coordinates of the second particle with respect to the first, we have six new variables with the properties summarized below:

Translational motion:			Rotation or vibration or both:		
Constants	x	y z	X	Y	Z
Variables	X	Y Z	x	y	z

If these new variables are introduced into (1) we get:

$$\frac{-h^2}{8\pi^2 M}\left(\frac{\partial^2 \psi}{\partial X^2} + \frac{\partial^2 \psi}{\partial Y^2} + \frac{\partial^2 \psi}{\partial Z^2}\right) - \frac{h^2}{8\pi^2 \mu}\left(\frac{\partial^2 \psi}{\partial x^2} + \frac{\partial^2 \psi}{\partial y^2} + \frac{\partial^2 \psi}{\partial z^2}\right) + (V(r) - E)\,\psi = 0 \tag{2}$$

where $\mu = m_1 m_2 / (m_1 + m_2)$.

The wave-function ψ is a function of all six coordinates X, Y, Z, x, y, z, but it is easy to show that a satisfactory solution to (2) will be a product of two functions, $\psi_t(X, Y, Z)$ $\psi_{r,v}(x, y, z)$. We introduce the product and then divide through by it and obtain (3):

$$\underbrace{\frac{-h^2}{8\pi^2 M}\frac{1}{\psi_t}\left(\frac{\partial^2 \psi_t}{\partial X^2} + \frac{\partial^2 \psi_t}{\partial Y^2} + \frac{\partial^2 \psi_t}{\partial Z^2}\right)}_{\text{I}}$$

$$\underbrace{-\frac{h^2}{8\pi^2 \mu}\frac{1}{\psi_{r,v}}\left(\frac{\partial^2 \psi_{r,v}}{\partial x^2} + \frac{\partial^2 \psi_{r,v}}{\partial y^2} + \frac{\partial^2 \psi_{r,v}}{\partial z^2}\right) + V(r) = E.}_{\text{II}} \tag{3}$$

Part I of this equation depends only on X, Y, Z and part II depends only on the variables x, y, z. Since X, Y, Z are independent of x, y, z we can write

$$\frac{-h^2}{8\pi^2 M}\frac{1}{\psi_t}\left(\frac{\partial^2\psi_t}{\partial X^2} + \frac{\partial^2\psi_t}{\partial Y^2} + \frac{\partial^2\psi_t}{\partial Z^2}\right) = c_{\mathrm{I}}$$

$$\frac{-h^2}{8\pi^2 \mu}\frac{1}{\psi_{r,v}}\left(\frac{\partial^2\psi_{r,v}}{\partial x^2} + \frac{\partial^2\psi_{r,v}}{\partial y^2} + \frac{\partial^2\psi_{r,v}}{\partial z^2}\right) + V(r) = c_{\mathrm{II}}$$

where c_{I} and c_{II} are constants obeying the relation $c_{\mathrm{I}} + c_{\mathrm{II}} = E$. The first equation clearly represents the translational movement of the molecule. c_{I} must be the eigenvalues E_{tr}. The equation is identical with (1), page 29 for $V = 0$.

c_{II}, therefore, must be the quantized, internal energy $E_{r,v}$. For the sake of brevity we now write E for $E_{r,v}$ and ψ for $\psi_{r,v}$ and get:

$$\frac{-h^2}{8\pi^2 \mu}\frac{1}{\psi}\left(\frac{\partial^2\psi}{\partial x^2} + \frac{\partial^2\psi}{\partial y^2} + \frac{\partial^2\psi}{\partial z^2}\right) + V(r) = E. \tag{4}$$

Equation (4) really is the one which is of interest to us now. We introduce polar coordinates as shown in fig. 14, and equation (4) becomes, transformed into (5),

$$\frac{h^2}{8\pi^2 \mu r^2}\left[\frac{\partial}{\partial r}\left(r^2\frac{\partial\psi}{\partial r}\right) + \frac{1}{\sin\theta}\frac{\partial}{\partial\theta}\left(\sin\theta\frac{\partial\psi}{\partial\theta}\right) + \frac{1}{\sin^2\theta}\frac{\partial^2\psi}{\partial\varphi^2}\right] +$$
$$+ [E - V(r)]\,\psi = 0. \tag{5}$$

As before, equation (5) becomes separable in the coordinates if we choose for $\psi(r, \theta, \varphi)$:

$$\psi(r, \theta, \varphi) = F_r(r) \times F_\theta(\theta) \times F_\varphi(\varphi). \tag{6}$$

Introducing (6) in (5) one gets after some rearrangement:

$$\frac{1}{F_\varphi}\frac{\partial^2 F_\varphi}{\partial\varphi^2} + \frac{\sin^2\theta}{F_r}\frac{\partial}{\partial r}\left(r^2\frac{\partial F_r}{\partial r}\right) + \frac{\sin\theta}{F_\theta}\frac{\partial}{\partial\theta}\left(\sin\theta\frac{\partial F_\theta}{\partial\theta}\right) +$$
$$+ \frac{8\pi^2\mu r^2}{h^2}\sin^2\theta\,(E - V(r)) = 0. \tag{7}$$

In (7), the term $(1/F_\varphi)\partial^2 F_\varphi/\partial\varphi^2$ is the only one depending on φ. As usual, therefore,

$$\frac{1}{F_\varphi}\frac{\partial^2 F_\varphi}{\partial\varphi^2} = k. \tag{8}$$

The general solution of this differential equation is

$$F_\varphi = A \exp i\sqrt{(-k)}\varphi + B \exp -i\sqrt{(-k)}\varphi \qquad (9)$$

where k must be real and negative (or zero) if F_φ is to be well-behaved. k is therefore written $-m^2$.

Since the solutions must be single-valued, they must be identical if φ is increased by 2π, i.e.

$$A e^{im\varphi} + B e^{-im\varphi} = A e^{im(\varphi+2\pi)} + B e^{-im(\varphi+2\pi)}$$
$$= A e^{im\varphi} e^{2\pi im} + B e^{-im\varphi} e^{-2\pi im}.$$

This is only possible for $\exp(\pm 2\pi im) = 1$, which means that $m = 0, \pm 1, \pm 2, \ldots$; m is the so-called *magnetic quantum number*. The reason for this name will be discussed later.

Introducing $-m^2$ in (7) in accordance with (8) and rearranging slightly we obtain (10):

$$\underbrace{\frac{1}{F_r}\frac{\partial}{\partial r}\left(r^2\frac{\partial F_r}{\partial r}\right) + \frac{8\pi\mu r^2}{h^2}\left(E - V(r)\right) +}_{\text{I}}$$

$$\underbrace{+ \frac{1}{F_\theta \sin\theta}\frac{\partial}{\partial \theta}\left(\sin\theta\frac{\partial F_\theta}{\partial \theta}\right) - \frac{m^2}{\sin^2\theta} = 0 \,.}_{\text{II}} \qquad (10)$$

Here, again, there is a part, I, only depending on r and another part, II, depending only on θ. These parts are, therefore, separately set equal to constants β, and $-\beta$, which gives (11) and (12):

$$\frac{1}{\sin\theta}\frac{\partial}{\partial \theta}\left(\sin\theta\frac{\partial F_\theta}{\partial \theta}\right) - \frac{m^2}{\sin^2\theta}F_\theta + \beta F_\theta = 0 \qquad (11)$$

$$\frac{\partial}{\partial r}\left(r^2\frac{\partial F_r}{\partial r}\right) + \frac{8\pi^2\mu r^2}{h^2}[E - V(r)]\,F_r - \beta F_r = 0 \,. \qquad (12)$$

If we introduce the permissible values of m into (11), it can be shown that the constant β, in the same way as m, may assume certain values, namely $l(l+1)$, where $l = 0, 1, 2, 3, \ldots$ if the wave-functions (F_θ) are to be well-behaved. A new quantum number l, the *azimuthal quantum number*, is thus introduced. m may take the integral values from $-l$ to $+l$, i.e.

$$l = |m|, |m| + 1, |m| + 2, \ldots \text{ or, } |m| \leqslant l.$$

At this stage of the problem no upper limit can be given to l. The F_θ-functions are *finite* series:

$$F_\theta = \sin^{|m|}\theta[d_0 + d_2\cos^2\theta + d_4\cos^4\theta\ldots + d_{l-|m|}\cos^{l-|m|}\theta]$$

if $l - |m|$ is *even*,

$$F_\theta = \sin^{|m|}\theta[d_1\cos\theta + d_3\cos^3\theta\ldots + d_{l-|m|}\cos^{l-|m|}\theta]$$

if $l - |m|$ is *odd*.

The ratio of successive coefficients can be calculated by the formula:

$$\frac{d_p}{d_{p-2}} = \frac{(p - 2 + |m| + 1)(p - 2 + |m|) - l(l+1)}{p(p-1)}.$$

Table IV gives some of the simpler F_θ-functions.

TABLE IV

F_θ-FUNCTIONS FOR HYDROGEN ATOM AND DIATOMIC MOLECULE

l	m	$l-\lvert m\rvert$	Coefficients d	F_θ	F_θ normalized
0	0	0	d_0	d_0	$\frac{\sqrt{2}}{2}$
1	0	1	d_1	$d_1\cos\theta$	$\frac{\sqrt{6}}{2}\cos\theta$
1	1	0	d_0	$d_0\sin\theta$	$\frac{\sqrt{3}}{2}\sin\theta$
2	0	2	$d_2 = -3d_0$	$d_0(1 - 3\cos^2\theta)$	$\frac{\sqrt{10}}{4}(3\cos^2\theta - 1)$
2	1	1	d_1	$d_1\sin\theta\cos\theta$	$\frac{\sqrt{15}}{2}\sin\theta\cos\theta$
2	2	0	d_0	$d_0\sin^2\theta$	$\frac{\sqrt{15}}{4}\sin^2\theta$
3	0	3	$d_3 = -\frac{5}{3}d_1$	$d_1(\cos\theta - \frac{5}{3}\cos^3\theta)$	$\frac{3\sqrt{14}}{4}(\frac{5}{3}\cos^3\theta - \cos\theta)$
3	1	2	$d_2 = -5d_0$	$d_0(1 - 5\cos^2\theta)\sin\theta$	$\frac{\sqrt{42}}{8}(5\cos^2\theta - 1)\sin\theta$
J	M	$J-\lvert M\rvert$	(usual quantum number designation for *molecules* instead of l and m)		

If, finally, $\beta = l(l+1)$ is introduced into (12) we can write:

$$\frac{\partial}{\partial r}\left(r^2 \frac{\partial F_r}{\partial r}\right) + \frac{8\pi^2\mu r^2}{h^2}\, F_r[E - V(r)] - l(l+1)F_r = 0 \,. \qquad (13)$$

A distinction between the case of the hydrogen atom and the diatomic molecule must now be made in what follows since $V(r)$ is not the same in the two cases.

The hydrogen atom will be treated on page 38–48 and the diatomic molecule on page 48–51. A treatment of the hydrogen *atom* is convenient because concepts, indispensable in most molecular spectroscopic work, can here be presented in their simplest form.

II. 6. THE HYDROGEN ATOM

The potential energy function for a hydrogen atom is $V(r) = -e^2/r$. The problem of such ions as He^+, Li^{++}, etc. becomes formally the same as that for the hydrogen atom if $V(r)$ is set equal to $V(r) = -Ze^2/r$ where Z is the atomic number.

By looking at (13) we see that certain conditions must be imposed on E in order that the wave-functions may be well-behaved. It may be shown that the 'permitted' values of E are the following:

$$E = -\frac{2\pi^2\mu Z^2 e^4}{h^2 n^2}$$

where n is the *principal quantum number*, which takes the values $n = 1, 2, 3, 4, \ldots$. It alone determines the energy. Simultaneously, it is found that $n-1$ forms an upper limit to l, i.e. $l \leqslant n-1$.

The F_r-solutions form a finite series:

$$F_r = \varrho^l \, e^{-\varrho/2}(b_0 + b_1\varrho + b_2\varrho^2 + \ldots\ldots + b_{n-l-1}\varrho^{n-l-1})$$

where ϱ stands for $(2Z/na_0)r$ and $a_0 = h^2/4\pi^2 e^2\mu$ (the 'first Bohr radius').

The ratio between successive coefficients is given by:

$$\frac{b_{q+1}}{b_q} = \frac{q+1-n+l}{(q+1)(q+2l+2)}.$$

Table v gives simple examples of the solutions.

TABLE V

F_r-FUNCTIONS FOR HYDROGEN ATOM

n	l	$n-l-1$	Coefficients b	F_r	F_r normalized
1	0	0	b_0	$b_0 e^{-\varrho/2}$	$2\left(\dfrac{Z}{a_0}\right)^{\frac{3}{2}} e^{-\varrho/2}$
2	0	1	$b_1 = -\tfrac{1}{2}b_0$	$b_0\left(1-\dfrac{\varrho}{2}\right)e^{-\varrho/2}$	$\dfrac{\sqrt{2}}{2}\left(\dfrac{Z}{a_0}\right)^{\frac{3}{2}} e^{-\varrho/2}\left(1-\dfrac{\varrho}{2}\right)$
2	1	0	b_0	$b_0\varrho e^{-\varrho/2}$	$\dfrac{1}{2\sqrt{6}}\left(\dfrac{Z}{a_0}\right)^{\frac{3}{2}} e^{-\varrho/2}\varrho$
3	0	2	$b_2 = -\tfrac{1}{6}b_1 = \tfrac{1}{6}b_0$	$b_0\left(1-\varrho+\dfrac{\varrho^2}{6}\right)e^{-\varrho/2}$	$\dfrac{2}{3\sqrt{3}}\left(\dfrac{Z}{a_0}\right)^{\frac{3}{2}} e^{-\varrho/2}\left(1-\varrho+\dfrac{\varrho^2}{6}\right)$
3	1	1	b_1	$b_0\left(1-\dfrac{\varrho}{4}\right)\varrho e^{-\varrho/2}$	$\dfrac{4}{9\sqrt{6}}\left(\dfrac{Z}{a_0}\right)^{\frac{3}{2}} e^{-\varrho/2}\left(1-\dfrac{\varrho}{4}\right)\varrho$
3	2	0	b_0	$b_0\varrho^2 e^{-\varrho/2}$	$\dfrac{1}{9\sqrt{30}}\left(\dfrac{Z}{a_0}\right)^{\frac{3}{2}} e^{-\varrho/2}\varrho^2$

When more than one wave-function corresponds to the same energy we speak of *a degenerate energy level*. In the case $n=2$ we meet with this phenomenon. That is, corresponding to the energy

$$E = -\frac{2\pi^2\mu Z^2 e^4}{4h^2}$$

there are *four* different wave-functions (normalization omitted)

$$\psi(n,l,m) = \psi(2,0,0) \quad = (A+B) \times d_0 \times (1-\tfrac{1}{2}\varrho)e^{-\varrho/2} \tag{a}$$
$$\psi(n,l,m) = \psi(2,1,0) \quad = (A+B) \times d_1\cos\theta \times \varrho e^{-\varrho/2} \tag{b}$$
$$\psi(n,l,m) = \psi(2,1,1) \quad = (Ae^{i\varphi}+Be^{-i\varphi}) \times d_1\sin\theta \times \varrho e^{-\varrho/2} \tag{c'}$$
$$\psi(n,l,m) = \psi(2,1,-1) = (Ae^{-i\varphi}+Be^{i\varphi}) \times d_0\sin\theta \times \varrho e^{-\varrho/2}. \tag{d'}$$

The energy levels of the hydrogen atom are n^2-fold degenerate.

Let ψ_1 and ψ_2 be wave-functions with the eigenvalue E in common. Then

$$\mathscr{H}\psi_1 = E \times \psi_1$$
$$\mathscr{H}\psi_2 = E \times \psi_2$$

which means that $\mathscr{H}(\psi_1 + \psi_2) = E \times (\psi_1 + \psi_2)$ or, more generally,

$$\mathscr{H}(c_1\psi_1 + c_2\psi_2) = E \times (c_1\psi_1 + c_2\psi_2)$$

where c_1 and c_2 are constants. Obviously, every linear combination of ψ_1 and ψ_2 is also a wave-function. Hence, such wave-functions as (a)–(d'), lose their priority as *the* wave-functions. Because of this freedom of choice, the functions finally chosen may be taken so as to obey subsidiary conditions. One may, for instance, demand that the wave-functions be *mutually orthogonal*.

Two wave-functions are said to be mutually orthogonal if

$$\int_\sigma \psi_1 \psi_2{}^* \, d\tau = 0 \ .$$

Wave-functions belonging to different energy levels satisfy this condition automatically. If they belong to the same energy level, this is not necessarily so.

It is easy to see that (a) and (b) are mutually orthogonal and orthogonal to the other functions of the group. On the other hand (c') and (d') are not necessarily orthogonal. As the element of volume in polar coordinates is $r^2\sin\theta \, dr \, d\theta \, d\varphi$ the orthogonality condition is:

$$\int_0^{2\pi} (Ae^{i\varphi} + Be^{-i\varphi})(A^*e^{i\varphi} + B^*e^{-i\varphi}) \, d\varphi \int_0^{\pi} \sin^3\theta \, d\theta \int_0^{\infty} \varrho^2 e^{-\varrho} r^2 \, dr = 0 \ .$$

The integrations with respect to r and θ certainly give finite results. For the integral to be zero a suitable choice of A and B must be made. In order to make the choice we set

$$\int_0^{2\pi} (Ae^{i\varphi} + Be^{-i\varphi})(A^*e^{i\varphi} + B^*e^{-i\varphi}) \, d\varphi = 0$$

which requires that $AB^* + A^*B = 0$.

This equation is solved, for example, by $B = 0$ and $A \neq 0$. The revised wave-functions (c) and (d) are:

$$A e^{i\varphi} d_0 \sin\theta \, \varrho e^{-\varrho/2} \tag{c}$$

$$A e^{-i\varphi} d_0 \sin\theta \, \varrho e^{-\varrho/2}. \tag{d}$$

Two other forms are sometimes given instead of (c) and (d):

$$A \cos \varphi \, d_0 \sin \theta \, \varrho e^{-\varrho/2}$$
$$A \sin \varphi \, d_0 \sin \theta \, \varrho e^{-\varrho/2}$$

which are constructed by adding and subtracting (c) and (d).

Table VI gives the complete, normalized and orthogonal wave-functions of the hydrogen atom in the two lowest levels.

TABLE VI

NORMALIZED, ORTHOGONAL WAVE-FUNCTIONS FOR THE HYDROGEN ATOM

n	l	m	Wave-functions	Equivalent forms
1	0	0	$\dfrac{1}{\sqrt{\pi}}\left(\dfrac{Z}{a_0}\right)^{\frac{3}{2}} e^{-\varrho/2}$	
2	0	0	$\dfrac{1}{4\sqrt{2\pi}}\left(\dfrac{Z}{a_0}\right)^{\frac{3}{2}} e^{-\varrho/2}(2-\varrho)$	
2	1	0	$\dfrac{1}{4\sqrt{2\pi}}\left(\dfrac{Z}{a_0}\right)^{\frac{3}{2}} e^{-\varrho/2} \cos\theta$	
2	1	1	$\dfrac{1}{8\sqrt{\pi}}\left(\dfrac{Z}{a_0}\right)^{\frac{3}{2}} e^{-\varrho/2} \varrho \sin\theta \, e^{i\varphi}$	$\dfrac{1}{4\sqrt{2\pi}}\left(\dfrac{Z}{a_0}\right)^{\frac{3}{2}} e^{-\varrho/2} \varrho \sin\theta \cos\varphi$
2	1	−1	$\dfrac{1}{8\sqrt{\pi}}\left(\dfrac{Z}{a_0}\right)^{\frac{3}{2}} e^{-\varrho/2} \varrho \sin\theta \, e^{-i\varphi}$	$\dfrac{1}{4\sqrt{2\pi}}\left(\dfrac{Z}{a_0}\right)^{\frac{3}{2}} e^{-\varrho/2} \varrho \sin\theta \sin\varphi$

The reason for choosing orthogonal wave-functions will be made clear later.

Each state of the hydrogen atom may be referred to by giving its wave-function. Inspection of table VI shows, however, that even the simpler ones are rather complicated expressions. Although the wave-functions are indispensable in applications of a quantitative nature, it is very convenient that the quantum numbers n, l and m themselves suffice in many cases to indicate the character of the state. Furthermore, these quantum numbers can be given a physical interpretation that is easy to visualize.

For instance, the quantum number n may be thought of as approximately measuring the *average distance from the nucleus to the electron*.

It can be shown that this average, $\bar{r}$, is given by

$$\bar{r} = n^2 \frac{a_0}{Z} \left[1 + \frac{1}{2}\left(1 - \frac{l(l+1)}{n^2} \right) \right]. \tag{14}$$

The quantum number l also enters the relation, but it is of minor importance. In order to see how a result like (14) can be derived from the wave-functions, it is necessary to refer to an important relationship between the quantum-mechanical operators, the wave-functions and the corresponding eigenvalues.

Every theory must be able to indicate to what extent the results of experiments can be predicted. In quantum mechanics, where we have resorted to a probability density description, it might – at first glance – be assumed that predictions might always come out similar to (14), i.e. predictions of *average* values.

On second thought, however, we see that *definite energy values* were predicted. This problem, therefore, arises:

To which physical quantities may definite values be ascribed, and to which quantities only average values?

Let O stand for a 'classical' physical quantity like coordinate, momentum, energy etc. and let O be 'associated' with the operator O derived according to the rules I and II on page 26.

Now, if

$$O\psi = k \times \psi \tag{A}$$

the constant value k is predicted for the quantity O. – If

$$O\psi \neq k \times \psi$$

we can only calculate (and measure) the *average* value:

$$\bar{O} = \frac{\int \psi^* O\psi \, d\tau}{\int \psi^* \psi \, d\tau}. \tag{B}$$

Table VII gives a number of physical quantities *for a single particle* and their corresponding operators.

TABLE VII

CLASSICAL-PHYSICAL QUANTITIES AND QUANTUM-MECHANICAL
OPERATORS

Physical quantity	Operator	
	Cartesian coordinates	Polar coordinates
Coordinate x	x	$r\cos\theta$
Momentum $\boldsymbol{p}$ $\begin{cases} p_x \\ p_y \\ p_z \end{cases}$	$\dfrac{h}{2\pi i}\dfrac{\partial}{\partial x}$ $\dfrac{h}{2\pi i}\dfrac{\partial}{\partial y}$ $\dfrac{h}{2\pi i}\dfrac{\partial}{\partial z}$	
Angular Momentum $\boldsymbol{P}$ $\begin{cases} P_x = yp_z - zp_y \\ P_y = zp_x - xp_z \\ P_z = xp_y - yp_x \end{cases}$	$\dfrac{h}{2\pi i}\left(y\dfrac{\partial}{\partial z} - z\dfrac{\partial}{\partial y}\right)$ $\dfrac{h}{2\pi i}\left(z\dfrac{\partial}{\partial x} - x\dfrac{\partial}{\partial z}\right)$ $\dfrac{h}{2\pi i}\left(x\dfrac{\partial}{\partial y} - y\dfrac{\partial}{\partial x}\right)$	$\dfrac{h}{2\pi i}\left(-\sin\varphi\dfrac{\partial}{\partial\theta} - \cos\varphi\cot\theta\dfrac{\partial}{\partial\varphi}\right)$ $\dfrac{h}{2\pi i}\left(\cos\varphi\dfrac{\partial}{\partial\theta} - \sin\varphi\cot\theta\dfrac{\partial}{\partial\varphi}\right)$ $\dfrac{h}{2\pi i}\dfrac{\partial}{\partial\varphi}$
Energy $E = V + \dfrac{1}{2m}(p_x{}^2 + p_y{}^2 + p_z{}^2)$	$V - \dfrac{h^2}{8\pi^2 m}\left(\dfrac{\partial^2}{\partial x^2} + \dfrac{\partial^2}{\partial y^2} + \dfrac{\partial^2}{\partial z^2}\right)$	
$P^2 = P_x{}^2 + P_y{}^2 + P_z{}^2$		$\dfrac{-h^2}{4\pi^2}\left(\dfrac{1}{\sin\theta}\dfrac{\partial}{\partial\theta}\left(\sin\theta\dfrac{\partial}{\partial\theta}\right) + \dfrac{1}{\sin^2\theta}\dfrac{\partial^2}{\partial\varphi^2}\right)$

These rules we shall here take as mere postulates, by means of which the reader may, for example, easily verify (14), page 42. We shall demonstrate their use when a physical interpretation of the quantum numbers l and m is wanted.

Emission Spectrum of Hydrogen in the Field-free Case

In the highly evacuated hydrogen discharge tube collisions between atoms are rare, and the electric potential from the electrodes is insignificant compared to the internal potential $V(r)$. The Hamiltonian used on page 32 is, therefore, correct, and the wave-functions derived above certainly correspond to the conditions of the experiment.

Applying (A) we find, of course, that the energy of all states has a definite magnitude. Consistent with this the hydrogen (atomic) spectrum is strictly discontinuous in a large spectral interval. Besides the energy only the angular momentum, P, of the ground state $(n = 1)$ is definite $(P = 0)$. For all other quantities $O\psi \neq k \times \psi$, so that only average values are predicted. The ψ-function to use in verifying this in the case of a degenerate level is a combination of *all* the wave-functions belonging to that level because we cannot avoid having hydrogen atoms corresponding to all these functions simultaneously in an experiment. For instance, if an assembly of hydrogen atoms with $n = 2$ is considered one possible wave-function will be[†]

$$\psi_{n=2} = \tfrac{1}{2}(a + b + c + d)$$

where a, b, c, and d are the four wave-functions corresponding to $n = 2$, and given in equations (a)–(d), p. 39–40.

Emission Spectrum of Hydrogen in the Presence of a Magnetic Field

In this case several new lines are observed (*Zeeman-effect*). It is found that where a single line is observed in the field-free case usually a group of closely spaced lines occurs.

The quantum-mechanical treatment must, of course, start with a Hamiltonian like the one on page 32 but with a term added which takes account of the presence of the field. Let the intensity of the homogeneous magnetic field be H and let H be parallel to the z-axis of fig. 14. The new Hamiltonian operator we call $\mathcal{H}^{(H)}$, the wave-functions $\psi^{(H)}$ and the energy values $E^{(H)}$. Now, if $H \to 0$,

$$\mathcal{H}^{(H)} \to \mathcal{H}, \qquad \psi^{(H)} \to \psi, \qquad E^{(H)} \to E .$$

[†] Phase differences have been neglected.

For example, there are four wave-functions $a^{(H)}$, $b^{(H)}$, $c^{(H)}$, $d^{(H)}$, for which

$$a^{(H)} \to a, \quad b^{(H)} \to b, \quad c^{(H)} \to c \quad \text{and} \quad d^{(H)} \to d,$$

where a, b, c, and d are the wave-functions with $n = 2$ (page 39 and 40).

Solution of the equation $\mathscr{H}^{(H)}\psi^{(H)} = E^{(H)} \times \psi^{(H)}$ shows that the main effect of the field is to partly *remove the degeneracy of the energy levels* (in harmony with the experiment). Fig. 15 shows corresponding energy levels and wave-functions with and without field for $n = 2$.

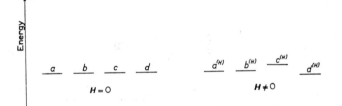

Fig. 15. Perturbation of hydrogen energy levels ($n = 2$) in magnetic field.

In the presence of the field $a^{(H)}$, $c^{(H)}$ and $d^{(H)}$ correspond to different energy levels. The wave-functions are, therefore, mutually orthogonal. For $H \to 0$, $a^{(H)}$ etc. converge towards wave-functions that are also orthogonal to each other. This is the reason why a, b, c and d of page 39 and 40 were chosen in the manner described.

As $c^{(H)} \to c$ for $H \to 0$, we may take $c^{(H)} = (1/8\sqrt{\pi})(Z/a_0)^{\frac{3}{2}}$ $\varrho \exp -\varrho/2 \sin \theta \exp i\varphi$ in *weak* fields. Let us ask for the physical quantities for which definite values may now be predicted. Since the levels are no more degenerate we may now operate on the single wave-functions.

$$\mathscr{P}^2 c^{(H)} = h^2/2\pi^2 \times c^{(H)}$$
$$\mathscr{P}_z c^{(H)} = h/2\pi \times c^{(H)}$$
$$\mathscr{P}_y c^{(H)} \neq k \times c^{(H)}$$
$$\mathscr{P}_x c^{(H)} \neq k \times c^{(H)}$$

which is easy to verify for the reader. For all the wave-functions of the hydrogen atom, $\psi^{(H)}$, it can be shown that

$$\mathscr{P}^2 \psi^{(H)} = \frac{h^2}{4\pi^2} l(l+1) \psi^{(H)} \quad \text{and} \quad \mathscr{P}_z \psi^{(H)} = \frac{h}{2\pi} m \psi^{(H)}$$

(compare table VII).

Consequently a definite value for the *total* angular momentum P and its *component* in the direction of a field, P_z, is predicted. The angular momentum, P, is quantized. It is now evident why we talk of l as the azimuthal and of m as the magnetic quantum number.

For the three states $b^{(H)}$, $c^{(H)}$, and $d^{(H)}$, $P = h\sqrt{2}/2\pi$ (since $l = 1$). P_z is, respectively, 0, $h/2\pi$, and $-h/2\pi$. The situation can be pictured as done in fig. 16.

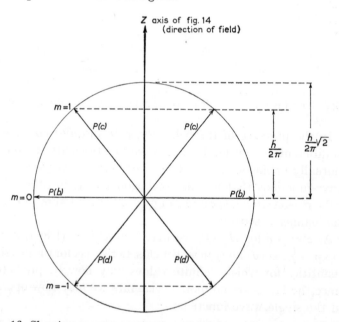

Fig. 16. Showing space quantization of total angular momentum P.

This phenomenon is generally called (external) *space quantization*. In terms of classical concepts the effect may be thought of as follows: for all states with $l > 0$ the electron produces a small electrical current in its orbit. In a magnetic field the energy of the atom depends on the mutual position of field and current. Classically, every position is possible, but quantum-mechanically only a few selected orientations are permitted.

Space quantization of the angular momentum is a very important phenomenon, also in *molecular* spectroscopy. Space quantization is caused by electric fields (*Stark effect*, compare chapter III) as well as by magnetic fields. The broadness of spectral lines must partly be due to the Stark effect which occurs when one molecule comes close to another, thereby entering the electrical field originating from the electrons and the nuclei of the other molecule. In this way the electric field intensity is varied continuously so that no new discrete lines occur, only a broadening of the 'undisturbed' line.

Of even more fundamental importance is what may be called 'internal' space quantization. As soon as more than one source of angular momentum is present inside the same atom or molecule, the momentum vectors are mutually space quantized, i.e. only certain mutual positions are possible. Several nuclei and all electrons possess angular momenta known as *spins*. Because of 'internal' space quantization there is only a selected number of ways in which these particles may be combined to form atoms and molecules. The hydrogen atom, for example, has an angular momentum in its electronic spin hitherto not mentioned.

If a beam of hydrogen atoms in the ground state (with angular momentum quantum number $l = 0$) is sent through a strong, inhomogeneous magnetic field, we would, from what has been said, expect the field to have no effect on the beam. The *Stern-Gerlach* experiment shows that the beam is split into two. This experiment, together with features from the hydrogen spectrum which cannot be explained alone by the $n-l-m$ description given above, makes it necessary to assume that the electron itself possesses angular momentum. Its magnitude is $|s| = h/2\pi\sqrt{\frac{1}{2}(l + \frac{1}{2})}$, often abbreviated to $s = \frac{1}{2}$. This spin may either be parallel or antiparallel to the angular momentum vector P which in this case is always indicated as l. The vector sum of l and s is called j, the total angular momentum vector, while l is the '*orbital*' angular momentum vector and s the spin vector.

Therefore, *four* quantum numbers, n, l, m, and j, are necessary to specify each of the states of hydrogen.

II. 7. THE DIATOMIC MOLECULE

For molecules, the quantum number for the angular momentum is not called l as it is for atoms, but J. Likewise, M is used instead of m (compare table IV page 37). Hence, the quantum rules for the diatomic molecule are:

The total angular momentum, P, is quantized and takes on the values

$$P = \frac{h}{2\pi}\sqrt{J(J + 1)} \quad \text{where} \quad J = 0, 1, 2, 3, \dots .$$

P is *space-quantized* and its possible components in the z-direction, P_z, are:

$$P_z = \frac{h}{2\pi}M \quad \text{where} \quad M = 0, \pm 1, \pm 2, \pm 3, \dots, \pm J .$$

Equation (13) page 38, after substitution of l by J, becomes:

$$\frac{\partial}{\partial r}\left(r^2\frac{\partial F_r}{\partial r}\right) + \frac{8\pi^2\mu r^2}{h^2}F_r[E - V(r)] - J(J + 1)F_r = 0 . \tag{15}$$

Studies of the pure rotational spectra of diatomic molecules have revealed that the interatomic distance r is *almost* independent of the state of rotational and vibrational excitation. Obviously, an important difference between the hydrogen atom and the diatomic molecule exists here [compare (14), page 42]. This difference must be used in the calculations to follow. Introducing $F_r = (1/r)f_r$ in (15) we get:

$$\frac{\partial^2 f_r}{\partial r^2} + \frac{8\pi^2 \mu}{h^2} f_r[E - V(r)] - J(J+1)\frac{f_r}{r^2} = 0 \, . \qquad (16)$$

For any diatomic molecule

$$E_{\text{rot}} = \frac{P^2}{2I} = \frac{P^2}{2\mu r^2} \, ,$$

where I is the moment of inertia.

As r is almost constant in the lower states of rotational and vibrational excitation it may be set equal to r_e, the distance in the equilibrium position (fig. 7, page 18).

Thus, as P is quantized:

$$E_{\text{rot}} = \frac{P^2}{2\mu r_e^2} = \frac{h^2}{8\pi^2 \mu r_e^2} J(J+1) \qquad (17)$$

which is identical with (2), page 17.

Writing (16) in the form

$$\frac{\partial^2 f_r}{\partial r^2} + \frac{8\pi^2 \mu}{h^2} f_r(E - V(r)) - J(J+1)\frac{f_r}{r_e^2}\left(\frac{r_e}{r}\right)^2 = 0$$

and introducing (17), we get (18):

$$\frac{\partial^2 f_r}{\partial r^2} + \frac{8\pi^2 \mu}{h^2} f_r\left[[E - V(r)] - E_{\text{rot}}\left(\frac{r_e}{r}\right)^2\right] = 0 \, . \qquad (18)$$

Setting $E = E_{\text{vib}} + E_{\text{rot}}$ we get (19):

$$\frac{\partial^2 f_r}{\partial r^2} + \frac{8\pi^2 \mu}{h^2} f_r\left[E_{\text{vib}} - V(r) + E_{\text{rot}}\left(1 - \left(\frac{r_e}{r}\right)^2\right)\right] = 0 \qquad (19)$$

which may also be written as:

$$\frac{\partial^2 f_r}{\partial r^2} + \frac{8\pi^2 \mu}{h^2} f_r\left[E_{\text{vib}} - V(r) + \frac{h^2}{8\pi^2 \mu r_e^2}J(J+1)\left(1 - \left(\frac{r_e}{r}\right)^2\right)\right] = 0 \, .$$

As $r \sim r_e$ we have that the term

$$\frac{h^2}{8\pi^2 \mu r_e^2}J(J+1)\left(1 - \left(\frac{r_e}{r}\right)^2\right)$$

may be neglected for small values of J. For small J-values, therefore,

$$\frac{\partial^2 f_r}{\partial r^2} + \frac{8\pi^2 \mu}{h^2} f_r (E_{\text{vib}} - V(r)) = 0 \, .$$

If we use $V(r) = \frac{1}{2}k(r - r_e)^2$ (Hooke's law, page 18), and if we introduce $x = r - r_e$ as a new variable we get:

$$\frac{\partial^2 f_x}{\partial x^2} + \frac{8\pi^2 \mu}{h^2} (E_{\text{vib}} - \frac{1}{2}kx^2) f_x = 0 \, ,$$

the important equation of *the harmonic oscillator*.

This equation has well-behaved solutions only if

$$E_{\text{vib}} = \frac{h}{2\pi} \sqrt{\frac{k}{\mu}} (n + \frac{1}{2})$$

which is (3), page 19.

Here, n is a positive integer or zero. It is noteworthy that the value of n represents no upper limit to J (as $n - 1$ does to l in the atomic case). Any rotational excitation can take place with any vibrational excitation.

The potential function $V(r) = \frac{1}{2}k(r - r_e)^2$ only reproduces the true potential function (fig. 7, page 18) near the equilibrium position.

Morse has constructed a mathematical expression which gives all the essential features of the $V(r)$-curve shown in fig. 7, page 18:

$$V(r) = D(1 - e^{-a(r - r_e)})^2 \, .$$

Here, a stands for $\sqrt{(k/2D)}$. We define

$$\nu_e = \frac{1}{2\pi} \sqrt{\frac{k}{\mu}}, \qquad x_e = \frac{h\nu_e}{4D}, \qquad B_e = \frac{h}{8\pi^2 c I_e},$$

$$D_e = -\frac{h^3}{128\pi^6 \mu^3 r_e^6 c \nu_e^2}, \qquad \alpha_e = \frac{3h^3 \nu_e}{16\pi^2 I_e D}\left(\frac{1}{a r_e} - \frac{1}{a^2 r_e^2}\right) .$$

Everywhere, the subscript e refers to 'equilibrium position'. For instance, ν_e is the vibrational frequency for infinitely small amplitude, or infinitely small vibrational energy. Because of the zero point energy the molecule never has an infinitely small vibrational energy. All the magnitudes with subscript e, therefore, refer to the so-called *hypothetical, vibrationless state*. Data for this state must always be obtained by extrapolation of data for 'real' states.

With this notation the energy, E, then becomes[†]

$$E = E_{vib} + E_{rot} = h\nu_e(n + \tfrac{1}{2}) - x_e h\nu_e(n + \tfrac{1}{2})^2 +$$
$$+ hc\,B_e\,J(J + 1) + hc\,D_e\,J^2(J + 1)^2 - \alpha_e(n + \tfrac{1}{2})J(J + 1)\,.$$

The two first terms record the vibrational energy. They reproduce the experimentally confirmed fact that the vibrational energy levels are not equidistant as (3) p. 19 indicates. Usually, however, the 'anharmonicity constant', x_e, is only 0.01–0.05. The next two terms give the rotational energy taking due regard to centrifugal stretching. They may easily be identified with the form used in the equation preceding (3), p. 19. Finally, the last term indicates that the vibrational and rotational energies are not completely independent.

Nothing can be said about *the electronic energy* of the diatomic molecule within the scope of this discussion since the molecule was initially idealized as a two-body problem instead of the actually occurring complex system of two nuclei and many electrons. To this degree of approximation the vibrational energy of the diatomic molecule is analogous to the electronic energy of the hydrogen atom.

II. 8. SELECTION RULES

Having found the atomic and molecular energy levels one might perhaps believe that the prediction of the entire spectrum would be easy. The emission and absorption frequencies to be expected in experiments would simply be all possible energy level differences divided by Planck's constant.

However, experiments soon reveal that this is not so. Generally, the number of spectral lines found is *far less* than expected according to the view above. This must mean that

[†] The difference between D (dissociation energy) and D_e must be noted.

usually a great many transitions between energy levels for some reason or another cannot take place, at least not by the emission or the absorption of electromagnetic radiation. Such transitions are spoken of as 'forbidden'.

The rules that state which transitions give rise to spectral activity are called *the selection rules*.

That such rules must exist can be predicted on a purely classical basis. In classical theory the electric dipole, changing its position in space or its magnitude (or both) periodically, is a well-understood source of electromagnetic radiation. If the frequency of the periodic motion is ν_m, the frequency of the emitted radiation is also ν_m. In reverse, the same rotor or oscillator only absorbs radiation of frequency ν_m. By means of this simple consideration many of the spectroscopic selection rules can be deduced.

Thus, for example, molecules without a permanent electric dipole moment (μ) must be expected to possess no pure rotational spectrum. Conversely, molecules with $\mu \neq 0$ must have a rotational spectrum. Molecules with $\mu = 0$ can show infrared absorption if they have normal vibrations which induce electric dipole moments (fig. 17).

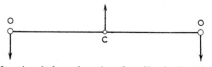

Fig. 17. Showing infrared active 'bending' vibration of CO_2.
$\mu(CO_2) = 0$.

Moreover, for molecules with $\mu \neq 0$, not all the $3N - 6$ normal vibration frequencies (p. 20) need occur in the spectrum, since in some instances a normal vibration may induce *no* electric dipole moment (fig. 18).

All these rules are, indeed, verified by experiments. No such simple picture can be used, however, for deriving the selection rules for the electronic transitions, simply because no reliable classical picture exists of the 'motion' of the electrons.

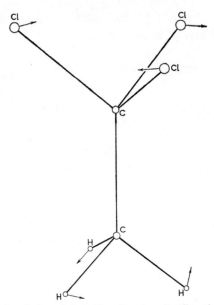

Fig. 18. Showing infrared inactive 'torsional' vibration of CH_3CCl_3.
$\mu(CH_3CCl_3) \neq 0$.

We shall try to sketch how the selection rules result from quantum mechanics. The difficulties in doing this are not rendered less by the fact that no completely satisfactory theory for the interaction between radiation and matter has been developed.

In the equation $\mathscr{H}\psi = E \times \psi$ introduced on page 28, ψ is a function of the coordinates, q, only. Let this be stressed by writing

$$\mathscr{H}\psi(q) = E \times \psi(q) . \tag{1}$$

The $\psi(q)$'s satisfying this equation are the time-*independent* wave-functions of the stationary states of energy E.

Of course, a more fundamental equation somehow must include the time, and it must be possible to derive (1) from it by asking for the stationary states. This fundamental equation is (2):

$$\mathscr{H}\,\psi(q,t) = \frac{ih}{2\pi}\frac{\partial\psi(q,t)}{\partial t} . \tag{2}$$

Let us investigate if (2) has solutions of the general form $\psi(q)f(t)$ where $\psi(q)$ is the $\psi(q)$ of (1). As

$$\mathscr{H}[\psi(q)\,f(t)] = f(t)\mathscr{H}\psi(q) \quad \text{and} \quad \frac{ih}{2\pi}\frac{\partial}{\partial t}[\psi(q)\,f(t)] = \psi(q)\frac{ih}{2\pi}\frac{\partial}{\partial t}f(t)$$

we get

$$\frac{1}{\psi(q)}\mathscr{H}\psi(q) = \frac{ih}{2\pi}\frac{1}{f(t)}\frac{\partial f(t)}{\partial t}.$$

Since coordinates and time are independent variables, each side of this equation must, therefore, be constant. Setting

$$\frac{1}{\psi(q)}\mathscr{H}\psi(q) = k$$

we realize by comparison with (1) that k must be the energy E. Setting

$$\frac{ih}{2\pi}\frac{1}{f(t)}\frac{\partial f(t)}{\partial t} = E$$

which has the solution

$$f(t) = e^{-2\pi i \frac{E}{h} t},$$

we see that a separation of coordinates and time is possible and that

$$\psi(q,t) = \psi(q)e^{-2\pi i \frac{E}{h} t}$$

is a solution of (2).

Say, for the sake of simplicity, that we consider an assembly of molecules to which only two stationary states with energies E_m and E_n are available ($E_m > E_n$). Let the wavefunctions be $\psi_m(q)$ and $\psi_n(q)$, respectively. As long as the system is not irradiated it may be described by

$$\psi^0 = c_m\,\psi_m(q,t) + c_n\,\psi_n(q,t) \tag{3}$$

where c_m and c_n are constants that take into account the number of molecules in the two states. (3), of course, is a solution of (2).

Now, by irradiation the molecules come under the influence

of the electric field of the wave. The Hamiltonian operator, $\mathscr{H}$, must now be changed to $\mathscr{H} + \mathscr{H}'$ where $\mathscr{H}'$ is the operator of the potential energy of the molecule in the varying electric field of the radiation. (2) now becomes

$$(\mathscr{H} + \mathscr{H}')\, \psi(q,t) = \frac{ih}{2\pi}\, \frac{\partial \psi(q,t)}{\partial t}. \qquad (4)$$

(3) is, of course, not a solution of (4) but it may be made so by changing c_m and c_n so that they mean time-dependent functions. If this 'new' function

$$\psi(q,t) = c_m(t)\, \psi_m(q,t) + c_n(t)\, \psi_n(q,t)$$

is inserted into (4) we get

$$\mathscr{H}'\psi(q,t) = \frac{ih}{2\pi}\left[\frac{\partial c_m}{\partial t}\, \psi_m(q,t) + \frac{\partial c_n}{\partial t}\, \psi_n(q,t)\right].$$

Both sides of this equation are now multiplied by $\psi_m{}^*(q,t)$ and integrated over the configuration space. This gives the relation

$$c_m(t) \int \psi_m{}^*(q,t)\, \mathscr{H}'\psi_m(q,t)\, \mathrm{d}\tau + c_n(t) \int \psi_m{}^*(q,t)\, \mathscr{H}'\psi_n(q,t)\, \mathrm{d}\tau = \frac{ih}{2\pi}\, \frac{\partial c_m(t)}{\partial t}$$

or

$$\frac{\partial c_m(t)}{\partial t} = \frac{2\pi}{ih}\left[c_m(t) \int \psi_m{}^*(q,t)\mathscr{H}'\psi_m(q,t)\, \mathrm{d}\tau + c_n(t) \int \psi_m{}^*(q,t)\, \mathscr{H}'\psi_n(q,t)\, \mathrm{d}\tau\right].$$

In order to get the decisive equations without too much mathematics the following discussion is somewhat over-simplified. Say, that c_m is zero at the beginning of an experiment. If transitions to the upper state are possible it means that

$$\frac{\partial c_m(t)}{\partial t} = \frac{2\pi}{ih}\, c_n \int_\sigma \psi_m{}^*(q,t)\, \mathscr{H}'\psi_n(q,t)\, \mathrm{d}\tau \qquad (5)$$

must differ from zero.

As demonstrated on page 34, $\psi(q)$ can be written as a product of a function, $\psi(X,Y,Z)$, depending only on the coordinates of the center of gravity (X,Y,Z), and a function $\psi(x,y,z)$

which depends only on the 'internal' coordinates. We have, therefore:

$$\psi_m(q,t) = \psi_m(X,Y,Z)\,\psi_m(x,y,z)\mathrm{e}^{-2\pi\mathrm{i}\frac{E_m}{h}t}$$

and

$$\psi_n(q,t) = \psi_n(X,Y,Z)\,\psi_n(x,y,z)\mathrm{e}^{-2\pi\mathrm{i}\frac{E_n}{h}t}\,.$$

As the wave-length of the radiation used in molecular spectroscopy is always at least 100 times greater than the dimensions of the molecule, the electric field intensity of the wave may be taken constant within the domain of a molecule. Let $\boldsymbol{\mu}$ be the dipole moment vector of the molecule and $\boldsymbol{F}$ the field intensity vector. Then $\mathscr{H}'$ is the scalar product of $\boldsymbol{\mu}$ and $\boldsymbol{F}$, or: $\mathscr{H}' = \boldsymbol{\mu}\cdot\boldsymbol{F}$. Here $\mathscr{H}'$ varies greatly from molecule to molecule because of the different mutual positions of molecule and field. While $\boldsymbol{\mu}$ is only a function of x, y, z, $\boldsymbol{F}$ is only a function of X, Y, Z. We can, therefore, write:

$\boldsymbol{\mu}(x,y,z)\cdot\boldsymbol{F}(X,Y,Z) =$
$\qquad \mu_x(x,y,z)\,F_X(X,Y,Z) + \mu_y(x,y,z)\,F_Y(X,Y,Z) + \mu_z(x,y,z)\,F_Z(X,Y,Z)$

where, for example, $F_X(X,Y,Z)$ means the X-component of $\boldsymbol{F}(X,Y,Z)$.

In this way (5) may be written as a sum of 3 integrals one of which is:

$$\frac{\partial c_m(t)}{\partial t} = \frac{2\pi}{\mathrm{i}h}\,c_n\mathrm{e}^{-2\pi\mathrm{i}\frac{E_n-E_m}{h}t}$$

$$\int \psi_m{}^*(X,Y,Z)\,\psi_m{}^*(x,y,z)\,\mu_x(x,y,z)\,F_X(X,Y,Z)\,\psi_n(X,Y,Z)\,\psi_n(x,y,z)\,\mathrm{d}\tau\,.$$

The integral with respect to X, Y, Z:

$$\int \psi_m{}^*(X,Y,Z)\,F_X(X,Y,Z)\,\psi_n(X,Y,Z)\,\mathrm{d}X\mathrm{d}Y\mathrm{d}Z$$

is seen to be common to all molecules. Clearly no individual selection rules can be derived from this. However, individuality enters into the integral with respect to the internal coordinates:

$$\int \psi_m{}^*(x,y,z)\,\mu_x(x,y,z)\,\psi_n(x,y,z)\,\mathrm{d}x\mathrm{d}y\mathrm{d}z\,.$$

It can be shown generally that if just one of the integrals:

$$\int_\sigma \psi_m{}^*(x,y,z)\, \mu_x(x,y,z)\, \psi_n(x,y,z)\, \mathrm{d}x\mathrm{d}y\mathrm{d}z = \mu_{x_{mn}}$$

$$\int_\sigma \psi_m{}^*(x,y,z)\, \mu_y(x,y,z)\, \psi_n(x,y,z)\, \mathrm{d}x\mathrm{d}y\mathrm{d}z = \mu_{y_{mn}}$$

$$\int_\sigma \psi_m{}^*(x,y,z)\, \mu_z(x,y,z)\, \psi_n(x,y,z)\, \mathrm{d}x\mathrm{d}y\mathrm{d}z = \mu_{z_{mn}}$$

differs from zero the transition is 'permitted'.

By means of the above expressions a number of simple selection rules can be derived. The reader can readily carry this out in the case of the hydrogen atom, since here $\mu_x = ex$ etc. We shall be satisfied with just quoting the most important of these rules:

The Hydrogen Atom

The quantum number n may vary unrestrictedly. l may vary by plus or minus one ($\Delta l = \pm 1$). The selection rule for m is: $\Delta m = 0$ or ± 1. Finally, $\Delta s = 0$.

The Diatomic Molecule

$\Delta n = \pm 1$. $\Delta J = \pm 1$. $\Delta M = 0$ or ± 1.

It is seen how drastically these rules influence the number of quantum transitions that may occur spectroscopically.

II. 9. INTENSITY OF ABSORPTION LINES

A gas, which for the sake of simplicity is thought to have only two quantum states, n and m, available ($E_m > E_n$) is enclosed by a perfect filter transparent only to radiation of frequency $(E_m - E_n)/h = \nu$. Gas and filter are surrounded by a perfect black body, and radiation equilibrium is established. Inside this system two sorts of emission take place from the gas via the filter to the black body:

a. 'Spontaneous' emission which would also take place if the intensity of the radiation from the black body was zero.

b. 'Induced' or 'stimulated' emission due to the presence of the radiation from the black body.

At equilibrium this emission is balanced by a reverse absorption of radiation quanta coming from the black body to the gas.

The spontaneous emission is proportional to the number of molecules in the upper state, N_m, so that the number of molecules, $Z^s_{m \to n}$, subject to this kind of transition per second can be written as:

$$Z^s_{m \to n} = A_s N_m$$

where A_s is the *Einstein* coefficient of spontaneous emission.

The 'induced' emission, in addition, is proportional to the radiation intensity $\varrho(\nu)$ where $\nu = (E_m - E_n)/h$. Therefore,

$$Z^i_{m \to n} = A_i N_m \varrho(\nu) .$$

The (induced) absorption gives rise to the relation:

$$Z_{n \to m} = B N_n \varrho(\nu) .$$

At equilibrium,

$$Z_{n \to m} = Z^s_{m \to n} + Z^i_{m \to n} .$$

By using the black-body radiation law

$$\varrho(\nu) = \frac{8\pi h \nu^3 / c^3}{\exp(h\nu/kT) - 1}$$

and quantum-mechanical theory it can be shown that

$$A_s = \frac{64\pi^4 \nu^3}{3hc^3} (\mu_{x_{mn}}^2 + \mu_{y_{mn}}^2 + \mu_{z_{mn}}^2) \tag{1}$$

$$B = \frac{8\pi^3}{3h^2} \frac{g_m}{g_n} (\mu_{x_{mn}}^2 + \mu_{y_{mn}}^2 + \mu_{z_{mn}}^2) \tag{2}$$

$$A_i = \frac{8\pi^3}{3h^2} (\mu_{x_{mn}}^2 + \mu_{y_{mn}}^2 + \mu_{z_{mn}}^2) \tag{3}$$

where g_n and g_m are *the statistical weights** of the states n and m, respectively.

Now, although in an absorption cell of a spectrograph there is no radiation equilibrium or uniform radiation intensity, we may tentatively make use of the above relations between emission and absorption coefficients. In the first place this means that spontaneous and induced emission play very different roles in the various spectral regions since

$$\frac{Z_{m \to n}^s}{Z_{m \to n}^i} = \frac{A_s N_m}{A_i N_m \varrho(\nu)} = \mathrm{e}^{-h\nu/kT} - 1 .$$

In this formula T is the temperature of the black body which gives the same radiation intensity as the source of radiation of the spectrograph at the frequency considered.

In the microwave region where $h\nu/kT$ is about zero, $Z_{m \to n}^i \gg Z_{m \to n}^s$. In the visible-ultraviolet, where $h\nu/kT \sim 1$ they are equally important.

Since the induced emission is coherent with the incident radiation and adds to it, it may be said to diminish the absorption. We can, therefore, take

$$Z_{n \to m} - Z_{m \to n}^i = B\varrho(\nu)N_n(1 - \mathrm{e}^{-h\nu/kT}) \tag{4}$$

as a measure of the efficiency of the absorption spectrograph.

As the spontaneous emission is not coherent with the incident wave and is allowed to spread in all directions in most spectrographs the validity of (4) can be maintained for all spectral regions.

Therefore, (2) and (4) are the equations to be consulted if intensities of absorption lines are to be calculated.

It is interesting to see that, all other factors being equal, absorption spectrographs are about 50–100 times more effective in the visible-ultraviolet region than in the microwave region where the phenomenon of induced emission reduces the net observable absorption to about 1 per cent or less.

---

* When an energy level is g_n times degenerate (page 39) its statistical weight is also g_n. Therefore, $(N_m/N_n) = (g_m/g_n) \exp -h\nu/kT$ (Boltzmann statistics).

CHAPTER III

MICROWAVE SPECTRA

III. 1. RESEARCH POSSIBILITIES

This and the following chapters will be introduced with a review of some important features which must be taken into account in scientific and practical work in the spectral regions concerned.

No *microwave spectrograph* is commercially available at present (1961). Discrete spectra have only been reported for substances in the gas phase. In the condensed phases disturbances from adjacent molecules are generally large enough to completely 'blur' out rotational energy levels. Hence, discrete absorption lines probably cannot be observed. However, regions of *continuous* absorption may possibly be found for molecules in the condensed phases. Hitherto, studies have been concentrated on investigations of the discrete spectra of gases. Usually, gas pressures between 0.1 and 0.001 mm Hg in the gas cell are required. Besides gases, therefore, only vapours of liquids and solids with a vapour pressure of at least 0.001 mm Hg at the temperature of the gas cell can be investigated.

A further limitation of the research possibilities of microwave spectroscopy becomes apparent when one looks at the selection rules (page 52). (Readers who have omitted the reading of chapter II are referred to pages 51–53 for a short introduction to the concept.) For microwave studies these rules have the serious effect of excluding all molecules with a zero dipole moment. In practice this, of course, also means that molecules with *small* dipole moments may be excluded. At present, it seems as if a dipole moment of about 0.05 Debye is the lowest practical limit.

Among other circumstances to be considered, the question of the resolving power of the spectrograph and the molecular individuality of the microwave spectra seem most important.

The microwave spectral region extends roughly from 3000 to 300000 Mcsec^{-1} (0.1–10 cm^{-1}). As, on the average, two lines separated by $\frac{1}{2}$–1 Mcsec^{-1} can be distinguished separately, the microwave region has room for half a million lines. Therefore, the resolving power obtainable leaves little to be desired in the great majority of cases.

It is seen, by consideration of their origin, that microwave spectra possess a strictly individual character. With only few exceptions the absorption in this region takes place because the rotational energy of the molecules is increased. The rotational quanta are functions of the principal moments of inertia (compare page 63), which are themselves functions of the molecular bond distances, the bond angles and the atomic masses. The slight differences between the principal moments of inertia of isotopically substituted molecules are sufficiently great to produce differences of several hundred Mcsec^{-1} in the microwave absorption frequencies. Even molecules ordinarily considered to be identical, but differing in the orientation of a single atomic nuclear spin to the rest of the molecule, have separate microwave spectra. The microwave spectrum of a pure compound is, therefore, strictly individual*. As a practical consequence of this it may be predicted that the maximum number of traceable components in a gas mixture may be as high as 50–100, a performance which would scarcely be possible in any other type of molecular spectrum.

III. 2. ROTATIONAL ENERGY LEVELS FOR DIFFERENT MOLECULAR TYPES

As already mentioned the rotational energy quanta depend on the magnitude of the principal moments of inertia. These

---

* Microwave spectra (as well as infrared and visible-ultraviolet spectra) of d,l-isomers form obvious exceptions to this rule.

are defined as follows: $I = \Sigma_1^N m_i r_i^2$ is the moment of inertia of a molecule with N atoms about an axis where m_i is the mass of one of the atoms and r_i the corresponding perpendicular distance to the axis. If the axis goes through the centre of mass and if $\sqrt{(1/I)}$ is plotted along the axis (starting at the centre of mass), $\sqrt{(1/I)}$ describes an ellipsoid. Its axes are the *principal axes*, and the corresponding moments are the *principal moments of inertia*.

In the general case these principal moments of inertia are different. Conventionally, they are called I_A, I_B, I_C *in order of increasing magnitude*. Molecular symmetry, of course, plays a role both as to the positions of the principal axes and as to the relative magnitudes of I_A, I_B, and I_C. For instance, a symmetry axis of the molecule must always be a principal axis, and a molecular symmetry plane must be perpendicular to a principal axis. Table VIII summarizes the relationships between the principal moments of inertia in different cases of molecular symmetry. A, B, and C are defined by

$$A = \frac{h}{8\pi^2 c I_A} \geqslant B = \frac{h}{8\pi^2 c I_B} \geqslant C = \frac{h}{8\pi^2 c I_C}.$$

A, B, and C are usually called 'rotational constants'.

$\sqrt{A}$, $\sqrt{B}$, and $\sqrt{C}$ are proportional to the lengths of the axes of the momental ellipsoid.

A molecule is a symmetric top if it has an n-fold axis of

TABLE VIII

RELATIONS BETWEEN PRINCIPAL MOMENTS OF INERTIA AND MOLECULAR SYMMETRY

Moments of inertia	Molecular symmetry	Rotational constants
$0 = I_A = I_B = I_C$	Atomic case	
$0 = I_A < I_B = I_C$	Linear molecule	$A = \infty$. $B = C > 0$
$0 < I_A < I_B = I_C$	Prolate symmetric top	$A > B = C > 0$
$0 < I_A = I_B < I_C$	Oblate symmetric top	$A = B > C > 0$
$0 < I_A = I_B = I_C$	Spherical top	$A = B = C > 0$
$0 < I_A < I_B < I_C$	Asymmetric top	$A > B > C > 0$

symmetry and $n > 2$. If two such axes are present, the molecule is a spherical top. $CHCl_3$ is a symmetric top, CH_4 a spherical top molecule.

In what follows we shall give the positions of the rotational energy levels of linear molecules, symmetric top molecules, spherical top molecules and asymmetric top molecules separately.

Rotational Energy Levels of Linear Molecules

For a *rigid*, linear molecule*

$$E'_{rot} = BJ(J + 1) . \tag{1}$$

The rotational quantum number J takes on the values 0, 1, 2, 3... .

$$B = \frac{27.989 \times 10^{-40}}{I_B} \, cm^{-1} .$$

In the formula

$$E'_{rot} = BJ(J + 1) - DJ^2(J + 1)^2$$

regard has been taken to the effect of centrifugal stretching (compare page 19). D depends on the nature of the linear molecule. In the simple case of a diatomic molecule $D = 4B^3/\nu'$, where ν' is the wave-number of the molecular vibration. Usually the effect of the $DJ^2(J + 1)^2$-term is very small.

The physical meaning of the quantum number J may be explained to readers who omitted studying chapter II in the following way:

Let us consider a linear molecule, rotating in the plane of the paper about an axis through the centre of mass, T, as shown in fig. 19. The so-called *angular momentum* of the rotation is defined as

$$P = r_1 m_1 v_1 + r_2 m_2 v_2 + r_3 m_3 v_3 + r_4 m_4 v_4 + r_5 m_5 v_5 .$$

Its magnitude may also be expressed as $I\omega$ where ω is the

---

* Instead of the true energies, we generally give the energies divided by hc: $E' = E/hc$, i.e. the energy measured in cm^{-1}.

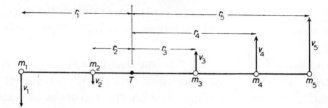

Fig. 19. Showing masses (m_i), velocities (v_i), and distances to centre of mass (T) for atoms of rotating linear molecule.

angular velocity. P is pictured as a vector, $\boldsymbol{P}$, perpendicular to the paper.

In classical physics the magnitude and direction of $\boldsymbol{P}$ may vary continuously, but according to quantum mechanics the *magnitude* of $\boldsymbol{P}$ is restricted to $(h/2\pi)\sqrt{J(J+1)}$, where $J = 0, 1, 2, 3, \ldots$. This is the physical meaning of J.*

Likewise, quantum mechanics shows that the $\boldsymbol{P}$'s for a group of molecules with the same rotational energy (i.e. common J) are not randomly distributed in space if an electric field is present. The $\boldsymbol{P}$'s of such molecules carry out precessional movements *around the field direction* in such a manner that the component of each $\boldsymbol{P}$ in the direction of the field takes on one of the values $(h/2\pi)M$, where M is one of the numbers $J, J-1, J-2, \ldots, 0, -1, -2, \ldots, -J$. The molecules are almost equally distributed among these $2J+1$ different states. This phenomenon, pictured in fig. 20, is called *space quantization*.

In very weak electric fields the energy difference between the various states is insignificant. In the field-free space each rotational level, therefore, consists of $2J+1$ coinciding states and is said to be $(2J+1)$-fold degenerate.

Symmetric Top Molecules**

$$E'_{\text{rot}} = BJ(J+1) + (A-C)K^2 \quad \text{(rigid, prolate symmetric top)} \quad (2)$$

---

* Most frequently, the angular momentum vector is called J instead of $\boldsymbol{P}$ but the designation above was chosen for the sake of clarity.
** In this case the rule $A \geqslant B \geqslant C$ is not always followed in the literature.

$$E'_{rot} = BJ(J+1) + (C-A)K^2 \quad \text{(rigid, oblate symmetric top)} \quad (3)$$

where $J = 0, 1, 2, 3,\ldots$ and $|K| = 0, 1, 2, 3,\ldots, J$.

The rotational energy here depends on *two* quantum numbers, J and K. The physical meaning of J is the same as above. The component of P *along the molecular symmetry axis z*, P_z, can only take on the values $(h/2\pi)K$. K, therefore,

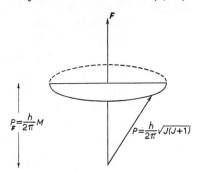

Fig. 20. Showing precessional movement of angular momentum vector P in electric field of intensity F.

is a measure of the angle between P and the *molecular* symmetry axis.

As usual, P is *space-quantized*. Because $E_{rot}(J, K) = E_{rot}(J, -K)$ each energy level is $2(2J+1)$ times degenerate, except levels where $K = 0$.

Spherical Top Molecules

Such molecules have no permanent dipole moment, and have therefore no microwave absorption spectrum. They will not be further discussed here.

Asymmetric Top Molecules

The energy levels of asymmetric molecules cannot be given by a single, explicit formula. As in the preceding cases $P = (h/2\pi)\sqrt{J(J+1)}$ where $J = 0,1,2,3,\ldots$. *In a field* there is space quantization as before. The degeneracy of an energy level is, therefore, $2J + 1$.

Table IX shows the positions of rotational energy levels for four different molecules, a linear molecule, a prolate and an oblate symmetric top, and an asymmetric top molecule. The magnitudes of the rotational constants are indicated in a qualitative manner at the bottom of the table. From what has been said the positions of the energy levels in the first three cases are obvious. The energy levels of the *slightly* asymmetric tops are also easy to derive. For a symmetric top $E_{rot}(J, K) = E_{rot}(J, -K)$, so that two states fall on top of each other. As soon as the top becomes but slightly asymmetric the levels are split so that a series of 'paired' energy levels exist, except for $K = 0$. In the general case, where A, B and C are significantly different, the energy levels must be shifted continuously if B is increased to A or decreased to C continuously. *Via* the 'paired' levels they must approach the levels of oblate and prolate symmetric tops, respectively. A rough approximation to the positions of the energy levels may be obtained by connecting the highest energy level of a group with common J-value on the 'prolate side' with the highest level of the same J-value on the 'oblate side', the highest-but-one 'prolate' with the highest-but-one 'oblate' etc. (inclined lines of table IX). The twofold degeneracy of the symmetric top levels with $K \neq 0$ must here be remembered. A labelling of the levels is now possible as the highest level of a number of levels with common J is called J_J and the others, in order of decreasing energy, $J_{J-1}, J_{J-2}, \ldots,$ $J_0, J_{-1}, J_{-2}, \ldots, J_{-J}$. One generally writes J_τ to identify the energy levels of an asymmetric top.

King, Hainer and Cross[*] have written the rotational energy levels of the asymmetric rotor in the form

$$E'_{rot} = \tfrac{1}{2}(A + C)J(J + 1) + \tfrac{1}{2}(A - C)E_\tau^J(\varkappa) \tag{4}$$

and have prepared tables of $E_\tau{}^J$ as a function of J, τ, and the 'asymmetry parameter' $\varkappa$:

$$\varkappa = \frac{2B - A - C}{A - C}.$$

[*] G. W. King, R. M. Hainer and P. C. Cross, *J. Chem. Phys.* **11**, 27 (1943).

For all types of asymmetric tops this parameter lies between
— 1 (prolate top) and + 1 (oblate top).

Another description, the so-called J_{K_{-1},K_1} description of a
rotational energy level, is now being more commonly used.
Here, K_{-1} is the K-value of the corresponding *prolate* top
$(\varkappa = -1)$, while K_1 is the K-value of the corresponding *oblate*

TABLE IX

ROTATIONAL ENERGY LEVELS FOR VARIOUS MOLECULAR TYPES

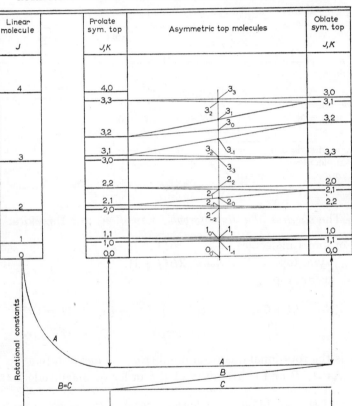

top ($\varkappa = +1$). The 3_3, 3_2, 3_1, 3_0, 3_{-1} etc. levels are now most frequently designated as $3_{3,0}$, $3_{3,1}$, $3_{2,1}$, $3_{2,2}$, $3_{1,2},\dots$ levels.

III. 3. SELECTION RULES AND ABSORPTION FREQUENCIES

The selection rules are summarized in table x. The last two columns do not concern us at present.

TABLE X

SELECTION RULES FOR ROTATIONAL ABSORPTION SPECTRUM

	Field-free case	F parallel to F_{mw}	F perpendicular to F_{mw}
Linear molecule	$\Delta J = 1$	$\Delta J = 1$ $\Delta M = 0$	$\Delta J = 1$ $\Delta M = \pm 1$
Symmetric top molecule	$\Delta J = 1$ $\Delta K = 0$	$\Delta J = 1$ $\Delta K = 0$ $\Delta M = 0$	$\Delta J = 1$ $\Delta K = 0$ $\Delta M = \pm 1$
Asymmetric top molecule Symmetry restrictions*	$\Delta J = 0$ $or \pm 1$	$\Delta J = 0, \pm 1$ $\Delta M = 0$	$\Delta J = 0, \pm 1$ $\Delta M = \pm 1$

The *spectroscopically observable transitions* are, therefore:

For linear molecules: $\nu'_{rot} = 2B(J+1)$ (5)

,, sym. top ,, : $\nu'_{rot} = 2B(J+1)$ (6)

,, asym. top ,, :

$$\nu'_{rot} = (A+C)(J+1) + \tfrac{1}{2}(A-C)\,[E_\tau^{J,+1} - E_\tau^{J}] \quad (\Delta J = 1)^{**}$$

$$\nu'_{rot} = \qquad\qquad \tfrac{1}{2}(A-C)\,[E_{\tau'}^{J'} - E_\tau^{J}] \quad (\Delta J = 0)^{***}.$$

J is the rotational quantum number of the *lower* state.

As A, B and C are often of the order of magnitude 2000

* G. Herzberg, *Infrared and Raman Spectra of Polyatomic Molecules* (Van Nostrand Comp., Inc., New York, 1945).
** So-called R-lines. The less frequently occurring lines with $\Delta J = -1$ are called P-lines.
*** Q-lines.

Mc sec^{-1} we see that there is about 4000 Mc sec^{-1} between succeeding lines in the microwave spectrum of a linear or symmetric top molecule. This is an extremely wide spacing in microwave spectroscopy. Therefore, usually only a few transitions will be observed, giving rise to a small number of microwave lines (plus possible 'fine-structure' components).

For asymmetric top molecules, the spacing which is controlled by $A-C$ and the bracketed quantities may assume almost any value. Often therefore, microwave spectra of asymmetric tops exhibit several hundred lines within a 1000 Mc sec^{-1} range.

III. 4. THE STARK EFFECT

The simple spectrograph shown schematically in fig. 1, page 8, can only be used for very strongly absorbing compounds. The absorption is small compared to the variations in klystron output for most molecules. As a feature, different from all other types of sample cells, the microwave gas cell is, therefore, generally equipped with a centre electrode, placed in the rectangular wave-guide (the gas cell) as demonstrated in fig. 21. To this electrode an electric field may be applied.

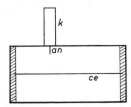

Fig. 21. Showing rectangular wave-guide (gas cell) cross-section, position of klystron (k), antenna (an), and center electrode (ce).

Let us assume that the molecules absorb microwaves due to transitions from state n to state m in the field-free case (fig. 22). These states are shifted to n' and m' in the presence of a field (the so-called Stark effect, compare page 47). Simultaneously, the microwave absorption is shifted from ν to $\nu^{(F)}$. Now, let the electric field be turned on and off periodically with frequency w. Absorption at the frequencies ν and $\nu^{(F)}$ now takes place and is interrupted w times per second, i.e., a frequency characteristic has been added to the absorption (but not to the noise etc.). The two signals may now be detected by an amplifier tuned to w. By this procedure most of the noise is not amplified so that very weak absorption may be detected in spite of the unfavourable background. The line at $\nu^{(F)}$ is called a 'Stark' component of the undisplaced line, ν. Generally, a line splits into *several* Stark components in a field. The counting of such components is an important step in the identification of microwave spectral lines.

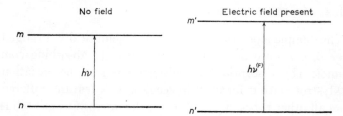

Fig. 22. Showing displacement of rotational energy levels (n and m) in electric field (to n' and m') accompanied by shift of frequency from ν to $\nu^{(F)}$.

It is readily arranged that the undisplaced line and the Stark components appear as deflections in opposite directions on the recording ammeter.

The Stark Effect of Linear Molecules

For the linear molecule with a permanent dipole moment μ the *change* in rotational *energy*, $E'_{rot}(J,M)$, in a field of uniform intensity F is:

$$E'_{rot}(J,M) = \frac{F^2\mu^2}{2Bh^2c^2} \; \frac{J(J+1)-3M^2}{J(J+1)(2J-1)(2J+3)} \; ;$$

$$E'_{rot}(0,0) = \frac{-F^2\mu^2}{6Bh^2c^2} \; .$$

In a field of intensity 300 volt per cm = 1 el. stat. c.g.s unit, a rotational energy level of a molecule with $B = \frac{1}{2}$ cm^{-1} and $\mu = 1$ Debye $= 10^{-18}$ c.g.s. units is shifted

$$0.000025 \; \frac{J(J+1) - 3M^2}{J(J+1)(2J-1)(2J+3)} \; \text{cm}^{-1}$$

or

$$0.75 \; \frac{J(J+1) - 3M^2}{J(J+1)(2J-1)(2J+3)} \; \text{Mc sec}^{-1} \; .$$

The selection rules may now be taken from the second and third columns of table X on page 68. F is the electric field intensity and F_{mw} is the electric vector of the microwave. Usually, F is parallel to F_{mw} in experiments. Here $\Delta J = 1$ and $\Delta M = 0$. Table XI gives calculated values of

$$\Delta \; \frac{J(J+1) - 3M^2}{J(J+1)(2J-1)(2J+3)}$$

for transitions with small J-values and F parallel to F_{mw}.

TABLE XI

VALUES OF $\Delta[J(J+1) - 3M^2]/J(J+1)(2J-1)(2J+3)$ FOR LINEAR MOLECULES

(Proportional to the frequency difference between the undisplaced line and the Stark components)

$M:$	0	1	2	3
$J = 0 \to 1$	0.5333			
$J = 1 \to 2$	−0.1524	0.1238		
$J = 2 \to 3$	−0.0254	−0.0071	0.0476	
$J = 3 \to 4$	−0.0092	−0.0056	0.0052	0.0288

We get, therefore, a qualitative picture of the spectrum, plotting the unperturbed transition as a line upwards, the 'Stark' components as lines downwards, as depicted in fig. 23.

This sort of Stark effect is called *quadratic* because of its dependence on the square of the field intensity. It gives rise to Stark components on both the high- and low-frequency sides of the undisplaced line. With increasing J the effect diminishes. Under the conditions mentioned on page 70 it

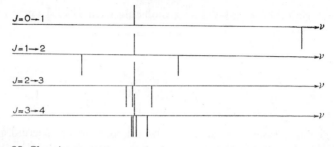

Fig. 23. Showing appearance of microwave spectra of linear molecules. Unperturbed line points upwards, Stark components downwards.

would only be about 0.01 Mcsec^{-1} for a $J = 3 \rightarrow 4$ transition. But the electric field intensity can be raised experimentally to a tenfold higher value in which case the Stark displacement would be 1 Mcsec^{-1}. This is about what it should be to be observable.

The Stark Effect of Symmetric Top Molecules

$$E'_{\text{rot}}(J, K, M) =$$

$$\frac{-F\mu}{hc}\frac{KM}{J(J+1)} + \frac{F^2\mu^2}{2Bh^2c^2}\left[\frac{[3K^2-J(J+1)]\,[3M^2-J(J+1)]}{J^2(J+1)^2(2J-1)(2J+3)} - \frac{M^2K^2}{J^3(J+1)^3}\right]$$

$$E'_{\text{rot}}(0,0,0) = -\frac{F^2\mu^2}{6Bh^2c^2}.$$

It is seen that for all levels with K or M equal to zero the first-order term vanishes and we get a Stark effect which is *quadratic* and of the same order of magnitude as for linear molecules. If, however, neither K nor M is zero, there is a large first-order Stark effect. Calculation of $-F\mu/hc$ for $F = 1$, $\mu = 10^{-18}$ gives 0.005 cm^{-1} or 150 Mcsec^{-1}. This should be compared with the 0.75 Mcsec^{-1} found for the quadratic effect. Neglecting, therefore, to a first approximation, the second-order term we can write

$$E'_{\text{rot}}(J, K, M) = -\frac{F\mu}{hc}\frac{KM}{J(J+1)}$$

where both K and M differ from zero.

The *changes* in absorption wave-number, $\Delta v'_{\text{rot}}$, due to the field and consistent with the selection rules $\Delta J = 1$, $\Delta K = \Delta M = 0$, are

$$\Delta v'_{\text{rot}}(J, K, M) = \frac{F\mu}{hc} \frac{2KM}{J(J+1)(J+2)}$$

where J is the quantum number of the *lower* state.

Table XII gives the magnitude of $2KM/J(J+1)(J+2)$ for low J, K, M-values.

TABLE XII

VALUES OF $2KM/J(J+1)(J+2)$ FOR SYMMETRIC TOP MOLECULES

(Proportional to the frequency difference between the undisplaced line and its 'linear' Stark components)

(K, M)	(1,1)	(2,2)	(2,1)	(3,3)	(3,2)	(3,1)	(4,4)	(4,3)	(4,2)	(4,1)
$= 1 \to 2$	0.3333									
$= 2 \to 3$	0.0833	0.3333	0.1666							
$= 3 \to 4$	0.0333	0.1333	0.0666	0.3000	0.2000	0.1000				
$= 4 \to 5$	0.0166	0.0666	0.0333	0.1500	0.1000	0.0500	0.2666	0.2000	0.1333	0.0666

As K and M may vary *independently* between J and $-J$, we get a *symmetrical* Stark pattern. The high-frequency part of this together with the unperturbed line is shown in fig. 24.

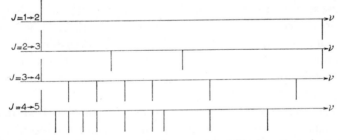

Fig. 24. Higher-frequency part of symmetrical Stark-pattern for symmetric top molecule. Linear effect. The quadratic Stark effect has been ignored.

For $F = 1$, $\mu = 10^{-18}$ and $(J, K, M) = (1,1,1) \to (2,1,1)$ the Stark component is 50 Mc sec^{-1} removed from the unperturbed line. These effects may, therefore, conveniently be studied at $F = \frac{1}{3}$ ($= 100$ volts per cm), while, as mentioned on page 72 a somewhat higher field intensity is necessary for the study of linear molecules.

Stark Effect of Asymmetric Top Molecules

The asymmetric rotor represents, of course, the most complicated example in which the Stark effect may occur. For complete details the reader is referred to the work by S. Golden and E. B. Wilson Jr.* For F parallel to F_{mw}, the following cases arise:

$$\Delta v'_{rot} = (A' + B'M^2) F^2$$

$$\Delta v'_{rot} = \pm F' |M| F$$

$$\Delta v'_{rot} = \pm G' \sqrt{(J+1)^2 - M^2} F .$$

A', B', F', G' are coefficients that are independent of M.

III. 5. INFORMATION ON MOLECULAR CONSTITUTION AND THERMODYNAMIC PROPERTIES FROM MICROWAVE SPECTRA

Molecules have long been known to be delicately balanced systems of positively charged nuclei and electrons. The presence of the electrons makes the great concentration of positively charged nuclei inside a molecule possible, and *vice versa*. The capture of the electrons by the nuclei, on the other hand, is prevented by the laws of quantum mechanics. We wish to examine how information on this complicated system may be acquired by molecular spectroscopy and how the 'internal' properties of molecules influence their behaviour when they appear in aggregates.

The stereochemists have succeeded in showing that it is reasonable to speak of a *nuclear framework* of a molecule. A similar idea has, however, never proved useful in the description of the electrons. As quantum mechanics indicates, we may at most expect to determine a probability density function of negative charge inside the molecular domain. This great difference in the behaviour of the two electrical counterparts is caused by their great mass ratio.

* S. Golden and E. B. Wilson Jr., *J. Chem. Phys. 16*, 669 (1948).

With reference to this, *microwave spectroscopy* may be said to furnish information on the geometry of the nuclear skeleton as well as to allow a determination to be made of the *electric field gradient* at various points of the molecule.

Since the beginning of microwave spectroscopy (1946) several hundreds of different compounds have been investigated, among which are many linear and symmetric top molecules. As seen from (5) and (6) page 68 only the rotational constant B can be found in these cases. If, therefore, a complete determination of the geometry of the molecule is desired, isotopically substituted molecules must also be investigated. In the hypothetical rotationless and vibrationless state (compare page 51) isotopic molecules have very nearly identical bond lengths and angles. This is not true, however, to the same extent in the ground state of the molecule. This state is not vibrationless (compare page 19). The data available are generally insufficient to permit extrapolation from the properties of the ground state to the hypothetical vibrationless state. Bond distances might be determined to 0.001 Å or less if this difficulty could be eliminated whereas, at present, most distances can only be given to an accuracy of from 0.003–0.005 Å. Table XIII illustrates the situation in the case of COS where B-data from *two* isotopic species are necessary for determination of both interatomic distances.

For large molecules (generally asymmetric tops), such as substituted benzenes, heterocyclic compounds etc. with many unknown bond distances and angles, the determination of three rotational constants is at most of value for a rough analysis of the structure. In such cases structural data from 'related' molecules may be assumed, leaving only three unknowns in the structure of the molecule under investigation to be calculated. This procedure is, of course, of only limited value. The correct procedure is to investigate a series of isotopically monosubstituted species. For example, in the case of propylene, $CH_3CH=CH_2$, one would have to examine the spectra of $^{13}CH_3CH=CH_2$, $CH_3{}^{13}CH=CH_2$, $CH_3CH={}^{13}CH_2$,

$CH_2DCH=CH_2$, $CH_3CD=CH_2$, and $CH_3CH=CHD$ in their vibrational ground state. By taking advantage of the observed *changes* in ground-state rotational constants as caused by monosubstitution, a so-called r_s-structure may be derived which is expected to deviate only slightly from the structure of the molecule in its hypothetical vibrationless state (common to all isotopically substituted species). Much work is in progress at present to clarify this situation*.

Information on the *electric field gradient* becomes available because several atomic nuclei possess a spin angular momentum I.

For hydrogen, $I = \frac{1}{2}$, for deuterium, $I = 1$, for chlorine, $I = \frac{3}{2}$ etc. The rotational angular momentum vector P and the spin vector I are 'internally' space-quantized.

TABLE XIII

INFLUENCE OF ZERO-POINT ENERGY DIFFERENCES ON CALCULATED INTERATOMIC DISTANCES**

Isotopic pair	C-O distance	C-S distance
$O^{16}C^{12}S^{32} - O^{16}C^{12}S^{34}$	1.1647 Å	1.5576 Å
$O^{16}C^{12}S^{32} - O^{16}C^{13}S^{32}$	1.1629 Å	1.5591 Å
$O^{16}C^{12}S^{34} - O^{16}C^{13}S^{34}$	1.1625 Å	1.5594 Å
$O^{16}C^{12}S^{32} - O^{18}C^{12}S^{32}$	1.1552 Å	1.5653 Å

The scalar value of $P + I$ is allowed only to assume the values $J+I, J+I-1, \ldots, |J-I|$. If I is less than J, $2I + 1$ states of different energy result. Now, the energy differences, of course, depend on the structure of the spinning nucleus and the molecular field at the location of the nucleus concerned. For the sake of simplicity efforts have been concentrated mainly on examples in which a single spinning nucleus is present in a linear or symmetric top molecule, on the axis of the latter. If $I \geqslant 1$, the spinning nucleus may possess a *quadrupole moment*, eQ, defined by:

* C. C. Costain, *J. Chem. Phys.* 29, 864 (1958).
** From a paper by C. H. Townes, A. N. Holden, and F. R. Merritt, *Phys. Rev. 73*, 1113 (1948).

$$eQ = \int (3z^2 - r^2)\, \mathrm{d}e$$

where $\mathrm{d}e$ is a charge element of the nucleus and $r^2 = x^2 + y^2 + z^2$. x, y, z are the coordinates of the charge element in a coordinate system with its origin at the centre of the nucleus and e is the electronic charge. If eQ differs from zero a change in energy, $\Delta E'$, results, given by

$$\Delta E' = \frac{eQ}{hc} \frac{\partial^2 V}{\partial z^2} \left[\frac{3K^2}{J(J+1)} - 1 \right] \left[\frac{\frac{3}{4}C(C+1) - I(I+1)\,J(J+1)}{2I(2I-1)\,(2J+1)\,(2J+3)} \right].$$

$$C = (I+J+1)(I+J+2) - I(I+1) - J(J+1)$$

for the case where P and I are parallel. V is the electrostatic potential from all charges of the molecule, except the nucleus concerned, at the position of that nucleus. z is the symmetry axis of the symmetric top. The case of a linear molecule is obtained if K is set equal to zero.

From the resulting 'hyperfine' structure of the microwave spectrum the product $eQ\,\partial^2 V/\partial z^2$ has been determined for a number of molecules. If eQ is known from other sources, $\partial^2 V/\partial z^2$ can be calculated, but even if this is not possible interesting comparisons may be made by studying a series of molecules which contain the *same* spinning nucleus. As eQ is constant throughout such a series, the variation in the product $eQ\,\partial^2 V/\partial z^2$ measures the variation in the field gradient. In table XIV

TABLE XIV

VALUES OF $eQ\,\partial^2 V/\partial z^2$ (IN MC SEC^{-1}) FOR
CHLORINE NUCLEUS IN VARIOUS POSITIONS

Compound	$eQ\,\partial^2 V/\partial z^2$
FCl^{35}	-146.0
Cl^{35} (atomic)	-110.4
ICl^{35}	$-\ 82.5$
$NC–Cl^{35}$	$-\ 83.2$
$HC{\equiv}CCl^{35}$	$-\ 79.67$
H_3CCl^{35}	$-\ 75.13$
H_3SiCl^{35}	$-\ 40$
H_3GeCl^{35}	$-\ 46$
$TlCl^{35}$	$-\ 15.8$
$NaCl^{35}$	0

chlorine and a number of chlorine compounds are compared.

As expected, $eQ\,\partial^2 V/\partial z^2$ is small for NaCl, where the chlorine nucleus is surrounded by a highly symmetric electronic octet, and large for atomic chlorine where there is a septet in the outer shell (here, $eQ\,\partial^2 V/\partial z^2$ has been found by atomic beam technique). For FCl, the constant is even greater than for atomic chlorine, thus demonstrating the great 'electro-negativity' of fluorine. There are molecules with bonds of partly 'ionic' character, such as TlCl and SiH_3Cl, between these extremes and molecules with 'covalent' bonds, such as ClCN and CH_3Cl. These interesting numbers have undoubtedly not yet been fully exploited.

Determination of the principal moments of inertia, I_A, I_B, and I_C is one of the most important steps towards a calculation of the *thermodynamic properties* of substances in the ideal gas phase. The thermodynamic functions enthalphy, entropy, and 'reduced free energy' are, respectively:

$$H^0 = H_0{}^0 + \tfrac{5}{2}RT + RT^2 \frac{\mathrm{d}\ln Z}{\mathrm{d}T}$$

$$S^0 = \tfrac{3}{2}R\ln M + \tfrac{5}{2}R\ln T - R\ln P - 7.267 +$$
$$+ \tfrac{5}{2}R + R\left(\ln Z + T\frac{\mathrm{d}\ln Z}{\mathrm{d}T}\right)\text{ (g cal)}$$

$$-\frac{(G^0 - H_0{}^0)}{T} = \tfrac{3}{2}R\ln M + \tfrac{5}{2}R\ln T - R\ln P - 7.267 + R\ln Z$$

for one mole of an *ideal* gas with zero-point enthalpy $H_0{}^0$ (part of which is vibrational), molecular weight M, and the absolute temperature T and pressure P in atm. These are seen to be calculable if Z and $H_0{}^0$ are known. Z is the partition function, defined as

$$Z = \sum_i g_i \mathrm{e}^{-w_i/kT}$$

where w_i is the energy of the ith rotational, vibrational, or electronic quantum level minus the zero point energy, k is Boltzmann's constant, and g_i is the degeneracy of the level (e.g. $2J + 1$ in case of a rotational level for an asymmetric top). At not too low temperature $(T > 100\,°K)$ Z is given to a good approximation by:

$$Z = \frac{0.006\,936 \times 10^{60}\sqrt{I_A I_B I_C T^3}}{\sigma} \prod_i (1 - e^{-h\nu_i/kT})^{-d_i}$$

if the molecule has no free or partly hindered rotation. Here, σ is the so-called *symmetry number*, which is the number of indistinguishable positions into which the molecule can be turned by simple 'rigid' rotations. σ is, for example, 2 for N_2, 4 for ethylene, 12 for methane etc.

The product $\prod_i [1 - \exp{(-h\nu_i/kT)}]^{-d_i}$ will be discussed later (page 99) but it does not deviate much from unity. Thus, the main determining factor is the product of the three principal moments of inertia.

The book by G. Herzberg* gives a treatment of the theory of rotational spectra. Also Gordy, Smith, and Trambarulo have published a book on the subject**. Another authoritative treatment has been given by Townes and Schawlow***.

---

* G. Herzberg, *op. cit.* (see p. 68 in this book).
** W. Gordy, W. V. Smith, and R. F. Trambarulo, *Microwave Spectroscopy* (John Wiley and Sons, Inc., New York, 1953).
*** C. H. Townes and A. L. Schawlow, *Microwave Spectroscopy* (McGraw-Hill Book Co., New York, 1955).

CHAPTER IV

INFRARED SPECTRA

IV. 1. RESEARCH POSSIBILITIES

Infrared prism and grating spectrographs are commercially available. The techniques of using such instruments may be acquired within a reasonable period, and, as a well-organized maintenance service has been arranged by the producers, infrared studies now compete favourably in number and importance with the earlier dominant investigations in the visible-ultraviolet region.

Several other factors co-operate to create the present powerful position of infrared spectroscopy. Spectra may easily be taken of compounds in all three states of aggregation. Furthermore, the selection rules have no serious effect on the research possibilities. As already mentioned (page 20), $3N - 6$ absorption lines (not including rotational fine-structure features) may be expected for a non-linear molecule with N atoms. Several of these transitions may be 'forbidden' by selection rules because of molecular symmetry (compare later), but not all of them, except in the case of homonuclear diatomic molecules. These have one normal vibration, which is forbidden.

The obtainable spectroscopic resolving power, conventionally defined as $\lambda/d\lambda$ (where λ is the wave-length and $d\lambda$ the minimum separation of two spectral lines which can be observed separately), varies, of course, greatly from one type of instrument to another and with the infrared spectral region under investigation. The resolving power for a very frequently used rock-salt prism instrument for the $3-15\,\mu$ region (part of the 'prism' infrared ($2-25\,\mu$)) is about 300, giving room for about 1000 separable lines. As to grating instruments, equipment with a 5–10 fold higher resolving power can be obtained.

Like the microwave spectra, infrared spectra have a strictly individual character. As stated on page 19, infrared absorption is due to an increase in the molecular vibrational energy, accompanied by changes in rotational energy. The presence of the rotational fine-structure will always guarantee the individual character of the infrared spectrum, but it is worth while noting that even without this fine-structure infrared spectra would still be fine 'fingerprints'. As the frequencies of the normal vibrations depend on the atomic masses and the valence forces, different compounds cannot have the same infrared spectrum. This is nicely confirmed by experience. Even very slightly different molecules, like naphthalene and mono-deutero naphthalene, have widely different spectra. Because of this circumstance prism instruments of relatively low resolving power still produce strictly individual spectra (where the rotational fine-structure is seen only as a broadening of the lines).

The maximum number of traceable components in a mixture investigated by a good prism instrument hardly exceeds 4–5. For grating instruments this number may be somewhat higher.

IV. 2. THE INTRAMOLECULAR FIELD OF FORCE

As already mentioned on page 63 microwave investigations have shown that the centrifugal stretching constant D usually is very small, which means that the positions of the nuclei are generally altered only slightly when a *rotational* quantum is absorbed. Consequently, the electron distribution remains almost the same.

Microwave spectra of molecules in excited *vibrational* states show that absorption of a radiation quantum from the infrared region causes much larger displacements of the nuclei. These displacements are, of course, balanced by a corresponding change in electronic distribution. As more and more vibrational quanta are absorbed, the molecule tends to dissociate. From this consideration we see that what we really want to have are formulae somehow connecting internuclear distances and electronic distribution with the magnitude of the infrared quanta which the molecule can absorb.

When an attempt is made to find these equations, enormous mathematical difficulties are encountered. The above picture of the molecule has, therefore, had to be simplified. Instead of the idea of the molecule as a nuclear framework stabilized by an electronic 'cloud', the picture of neutral atoms kept together by elastic forces has had to be used. This simplification is so radical that the role of the nuclei and the electrons is considerably obscured.

However, further simplifications are necessary if theory and experiments are to meet. As stated in the case of a *diatomic* molecule (page 18), *one* so-called force-constant sufficed to describe the elastic properties of the molecule. Of course, several constants are necessary for a molecule with many atoms. If we knew all these constants (which amounts to knowing the work necessary to distort the molecule in a random way), the frequencies of the normal vibrations could easily be calculated. The problem is, however, always the opposite: the infrared absorption frequencies have been found and the magnitudes of the force-constants are desired.

In the literature, equations relating infrared absorption frequencies to force-constants and masses for various molecules can be found. This might leave the impression that in the same way as the rotational constants A, B and C can be calculated if the microwave spectrum of an asymmetric top molecule has been properly analyzed, a complete set of force-constants may be computed by means of complete infrared data. This is nearly never so for the following reason:

Let W be the work necessary to displace the atoms from the position in which all the elastic forces are zero ('equilibrium' position or 'hypothetical vibrationless ground state'). W, of course, is a function of all the displacement coordinates, the differences between the actual and the equilibrium coordinates. Let these coordinates be (x_i, y_i, z_i) for the ith atom. We write $W(x_i, y_i, z_i)$ where x_i etc., stand for *all* $3N$ displacement coordinates (the molecule has N atoms). Of course, $W(0, 0, 0) = 0$. We now want to write W in a simple form which must be approximately correct for small values of the displacement coordinates. Let us write:

$$W(x_i y_i z_i) = \begin{cases} b_1 x_1 + b_2 y_1 + b_3 z_1 + b_4 x_2 \ldots \text{(first-order terms)} \\[2mm] + a_{11} x_1{}^2 + a_{12} x_1 y_1 + a_{13} x_1 z_1 \ldots \text{(second-order)} \\[2mm] + c_{111} x_1{}^3 + c_{112} x_1{}^2 y_1 + c_{113} x_1{}^2 z_1 \ldots \text{(third-order)} \\[1mm] \hspace{3cm} \text{etc.} \end{cases}$$

Now, $-\partial W/\partial x_i$ etc. is the x_i-component of the restoring force on the ith atom. This force is zero in the equilibrium position, i.e. for all displacement coordinates equal to zero. Therefore, W cannot contain any first-order terms. $b_i = 0$.

If we neglect the third and higher-order terms, W is reduced to a homogeneous, quadratic expression. The coefficients a_{ij} are the force-constants. If the molecule has N atoms, W contains $\frac{3}{2}N(3N+1)$ force-constants. However, W is not a function of $3N$ *independent* variables because three of the displacements of the molecule are just translations of the molecule as a whole and three others are just rotations (for linear molecules: two rotations). In all these six (five) cases, W is zero. W, therefore, really only depends on $3N-6$ (or $3N-5$) independent coordinates and may consequently be formulated as a quadratic function of these variables and $\frac{3}{2}(N-2)(3N-5)$ force-constants ($\frac{1}{2}(3N-5)(3N-4)$ for linear molecules.)

As mentioned on page 20 we cannot expect to observe more than $3N-6$ normal vibration frequencies. Generally, therefore, the experimental material is far too small for a calculation of a complete set of force-constants. In case of a molecule with four atoms, 21 force-constants are necessary, but the experimental material includes only 6 frequencies. In a very

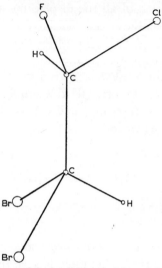

Fig. 25. Molecular model of 1-fluoro-1-chloro-2,2-dibromoethane.

limited number of cases this difficulty has been solved by studies of isotopic molecules which have the same W-function (with the same force-constants) but, of course, different vibrational frequencies because of the mass differences. It should also be noted that some of the constants, a_{ij}, of the cross-terms $(a_{ij}x_iy_j)$ in the potential function may sometimes be calculated by considering the changes in electronic distribution due to the molecular vibrations*. However, in the majority of cases a new sacrifice in accuracy must be made.

The manner by which one proceeds is to try to find out if some of the a_{ij}'s are greater than others which may, therefore, be ignored. The simplified method which has proved to be of great use (at least in the treatment of many non-aromatic compounds) has been formed on the basis of the idea that W can be written as a function of changes in chemical bond lengths and bond angles. This is the so-called valence-force method.

The simplification thereby obtained is seen by considering

* J. W. Linnett, *Trans. Faraday Soc. 44*, 556 (1948) and following papers.

fig. 25. The general quadratic work (or, potential-) function W of $CHFClCHBr_2$ has 171 constants. The experimental material includes 18 normal vibrational frequencies. If the problem is treated by the valence-force method it is seen that 18 constants in the potential function are necessary since 7 distances between adjacent atoms and 11 valence angles may vary. These 18 constants may even be reduced to 16 if the reasonable assumption is made that the force-constants for the two C-H bonds are identical and that the same is true for the two C-Br bonds.

In this or some similar way we finally arrive at a picture of the intramolecular forces governed by a number of force constants which is close to the number of experimental frequencies.

Gerhard Herzberg (*op. cit.* page 68) has given a number of formulae connecting observed infrared frequencies with force-constants of various types of molecules treated by different types of potential functions (pages 148–184 of his book).

As an example, the formulae for the vibrational frequencies of the non-linear symmetric XY_2 molecule, treated by the valence-force method, are given below.

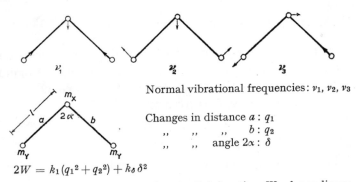

Normal vibrational frequencies: ν_1, ν_2, ν_3

Changes in distance a : q_1
"   "   " b : q_2
"   " angle 2α : δ

$$2W = k_1(q_1^2 + q_2^2) + k_\delta \delta^2$$

Fig. 26. Normal vibrations and potential function W of non-linear symmetric XY_2 molecule.

By inspection of fig. 26 the definitions of the symbols used in the following equation are seen.

$$4\pi^2 (v_1{}^2 + v_2{}^2) = \left(1 + \frac{2m_y}{m_x}\cos^2\alpha\right)\frac{k_1}{m_y} + \frac{2}{m_y}\left(1 + \frac{2m_y}{m_x}\sin^2\alpha\right)\frac{k_\delta}{l^2}$$

$$16\pi^4\, v_1{}^2 v_2{}^2 = 2\left(1 + \frac{2m_y}{m_x}\right)\frac{k_1}{m_y{}^2}\frac{k_\delta}{l^2}$$

$$4\pi^2\, v_3{}^2 = \left(1 + \frac{2m_y}{m_x}\sin^2\alpha\right)\frac{k_1}{m_y}.$$

In the case of water, $v_1' = 3652$ cm^{-1}, $v_2' = 1595$ cm^{-1}, and $v_3' = 3756$ cm^{-1}. Obviously, we can calculate k_1, k_δ/l^2, and 2α. The result is:

$$k_1 = 7.76 \times 10^5 \text{ dyne cm}^{-1}, \quad k_\delta/l^2 = 0.69 \times 10^5 \text{ dyne cm}^{-1},$$
$$\text{and } 2\alpha = 120°.$$

The result that the 'stretching' constant k_1 is about ten times as large as the 'deformation' constant k_δ/l^2 has been generally confirmed by studies of all different types of molecules. 2α is found to be 120° in fair agreement with the experimental value, 105°. It should be noted, however, that we are working in a very approximate manner, for, if one applies the same equations to the H_2S molecule, a valence angle of 156° (experimental value 92°) is found, and, indeed, in the case of H_2Se the calculated angle is imaginary.

IV. 3. VIBRATIONAL ENERGY LEVELS

If the molecule is treated by the methods of classical mechanics (in which case there is, of course, no hope of finding any discrete energy levels), the procedure is as follows:

The kinetic energy, T, is given by

$$T = \tfrac{1}{2}\,\Sigma\,m_i(\dot{x}_i{}^2 + \dot{y}_i{}^2 + \dot{z}_i{}^2)$$

where $\dot{x}_i = \partial x_i/\partial t$ etc.

Let the potential energy, W, be given by

$$W = a_{11}x_1{}^2 + a_{12}x_1 y_1 + a_{13}x_1 z_1 + a_{14}x_1 x_2\ldots$$

where the cubic and higher terms have been neglected.

As may be shown these $3N$ coordinates x_i, y_i, z_i can be replaced by $3N$ other coordinates, $q_1, q_2,\ldots, q_{3N}$ by means of a so-called linear, orthogonal substitution with the effect of removing all the cross-product terms from W (such as $a_{12}x_1y_1$) *without* introducing such terms in the expression for T. As a result of this substitution, therefore, we can write:

$$W = \sum_1^{3N} c_i q_i^2 \quad \text{and} \quad T = \sum_1^{3N} \tfrac{1}{2}\dot{q}_i^2 .$$

The linear, orthogonal substitution by which all this is attained can be written:

$$x_1 = d_{11}q_1 + d_{12}q_2 \ldots + d_{1,3N}q_{3N}$$

$$\vdots \qquad \vdots \qquad \vdots \qquad \vdots$$

$$z_N = d_{3N,1}q_1 + d_{3N,2}q_2 \ldots + d_{3N,3N}q_{3N} .$$

The c_i's and the d_{ij}'s are, of course, functions of the force-constants a_{ij}.

The $3N$ equations of motion are derived by using the Lagrange equation:

$$\frac{d}{dt}\left(\frac{\partial T}{\partial \dot{q}_k}\right) + \frac{\partial W}{\partial q_k} = 0$$

successively for $q_k = q_1, q_2, \ldots, q_{3N}$. One such equation is:

$$\frac{d^2 q_i}{dt^2} + 2c_i q_i = 0$$

which has the solution

$$q_i = q_i^0 \sin(\sqrt{2c_i}\, t + \varphi_i)$$

where q_i^0 and φ_i are constants of integration. Consequently,

$$x_1 = d_{11}q_1^0 \sin(\sqrt{2c_1}\, t + \varphi_1) + d_{12}q_2^0 \sin(\sqrt{2c_2}\, t + \varphi_2) + \cdots$$

$$+ d_{1,3N}q_{3N}^0 \sin(\sqrt{2c_{3N}}\, t + \varphi_{3N}) .$$

For the other displacement coordinates similar expressions are obtained. We see that the atoms carry out motions that may be regarded as being a superposition of $3N$ sinusoidal (harmonic) vibrations. By successively setting all the q_i^0's equal to zero except one, these fundamental vibrations can be studied separately. Their frequencies are $\sqrt{(2c_i)}/2\pi$ etc. They constitute the *normal vibrations of the molecule*. Among them, three translations and three rotations of the molecule as a whole will be found. In these cases the restoring forces will be zero, which means that the corresponding frequencies (or the c_i's) are also zero. Classically, therefore, all possible vibrational movements (of which there is, of course, an infinite number) can be said to consist of contributions from $3N-6$ normal vibrations.

Once the magnitude of the normal vibrational frequencies has been found the c_i's are known, permitting a calculation of the d_{ij}'s, except for a constant, and establishing numerical relations between the force-constants a_{ij}.

Quantum-mechanically the problem is treated in a very similar way. We have

$$H = \tfrac{1}{2} \sum_{1}^{N} m_i(\dot{x}_i{}^2 + \dot{y}_i{}^2 + \dot{z}_i{}^2) + a_{11}x_1{}^2 + a_{12}x_1 y_1 \ldots .$$

The Hamiltonian operator is, therefore:

$$\mathcal{H} = \frac{-h^2}{8\pi^2} \sum_{1}^{N} \frac{1}{m_i} \left(\frac{\partial^2}{\partial x_i{}^2} + \frac{\partial^2}{\partial y_i{}^2} + \frac{\partial^2}{\partial z_i{}^2} \right) + a_{11}x_1{}^2 + a_{12}x_1 y_1 \ldots .$$

If we use the $\mathcal{H}\psi = E \times \psi$ relation we get

$$\frac{-h^2}{8\pi^2} \sum_{1}^{N} \frac{1}{m_i} \left(\frac{\partial^2\psi}{\partial x_i{}^2} + \frac{\partial^2\psi}{\partial y_i{}^2} + \frac{\partial^2\psi}{\partial z_i{}^2} \right) + (a_{11}x_1{}^2 + a_{12}x_1 y_1 \ldots)\psi = E\psi ,$$

where E is the energy of the discrete levels we are looking for.
By means of the same substitutions as above the equation is changed to

$$\sum_{1}^{3N} \frac{\partial^2\psi}{\partial q_i{}^2} + \frac{8\pi^2}{h^2} \left(E - \sum_{1}^{3N} c_i q_i{}^2 \right) \psi = 0 .$$

Here, the variables can be separated by setting $\psi(q_1, q_2, \ldots, q_{3N}) = \Pi\psi(q_i)$. Because these variables are independent, $3N$ separate equations must be fulfilled:

$$\frac{\partial^2\psi(q_i)}{\partial q_i{}^2} + \frac{8\pi^2}{h^2} (E_i - c_i q_i{}^2) \psi = 0$$

where $\Sigma E_i = E$.
The eigenvalues of these equations are:

$$E_i = \left(\frac{h}{2\pi} \right) \sqrt{2c_i}(n_i + \tfrac{1}{2})$$

where $n_i = 0, 1, 2, \ldots$.
The radiation quantum absorbed, $h\nu_i{}^{(a)}$, when n_i changes by one, is $(h/2\pi)\sqrt{2c_i}$. In the classical treatment, the frequency of the ith normal vibration, $\nu_i{}^{nor}$, was $\sqrt{(2c_i)}/2\pi$. From this, we see that $\nu_i{}^{nor} = \nu_i{}^{(a)}$.

Quantum mechanics shows, therefore, that the quantized, vibrational energy, E_{vib}, of a molecule with the normal vibrational frequencies $\nu_i{}^{nor}$, is:

$$E_{\text{vib}} = hc[v_1'^{\text{nor}}(n_1 + \tfrac{1}{2}) + v_2'^{\text{nor}}(n_2 + \tfrac{1}{2}) \ldots + v_{3N-6}'^{\text{nor}}(n_{3N-6} + \tfrac{1}{2})] .$$

The $3N-6$ vibrational quantum numbers $n_1, n_2, \ldots, n_{3N-6}$ may independently be all integers including zero. We see that a rather large *zero-point energy* exists. Fig. 27 shows the situation for a non-linear triatomic molecule.

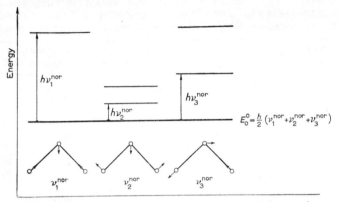

Fig. 27. Showing zero-point energy, E_0^0, normal vibrations and some of the vibrational energy levels of triatomic molecules.

Below the vibrational levels the corresponding pictures of the 'classical' normal frequencies have been placed. We shall see why these pictures are still very useful although they are arrived at in a somewhat unsatisfactory way.

IV. 4. SELECTION RULES AND ABSORPTION FREQUENCIES

Now that the vibrational energy levels have been given, the selection rules become of interest. For the *completely unsymmetrical molecule*, the selection rules for molecules in the gas phase are:

$$\Delta n_i = \pm 1 \quad \text{while} \quad \Delta n_j = 0 \quad (i \neq j) .$$

Only one vibrational quantum can be absorbed at a time. Classically, the rule means that $3N-6$ different absorption frequencies can be observed.

At this stage it is convenient to compare theory and experience. With reference to table XV, we see (3rd column) that in the typical experiment considered *more* than the expected $3N-6$ absorption bands have been found. This discrepancy shows that somehow we have been working with over-simplified ideas.

TABLE XV

SUPPOSED EXAMPLE OF EXPECTED NORMAL VIBRATION FREQUENCIES AND EXPERIMENTAL ABSORPTION FREQUENCIES FOR FOUR-ATOMIC UNSYMMETRICAL MOLECULE AND AN INTERPRETATION OF THE RESULTS

Frequency designation	Expected frequencies	Experimental frequencies	Proposed interpretation
ν_1	525 cm⁻¹	523 cm⁻¹	ν_1
ν_2	830	825	ν_2
ν_3	1005	1010	ν_3
ν_4	1200	1220	ν_4
ν_5	1500	1511	ν_5
ν_6	3315	3299	ν_6
		520	ν_1 ($n = 1 \rightarrow 2$)
		821	ν_2 ($n = 1 \rightarrow 2$)
		1040	$2\nu_1$
		988	$\nu_5 - \nu_1$
		1350	$\nu_1 + \nu_2$
		1520	$\nu_1 + \nu_3$
		1995	$2\nu_3$

The weak point in the derivation of the energy levels (page 86) is, of course, the assumption of a *quadratic* potential function. If it is assumed that third and higher-order terms in W cannot be neglected, an explanation of the appearance of the extra lines is found.

This is already seen by considering a diatomic molecule. For this, $E_{\text{vib}} = hc\nu'(n + \frac{1}{2})$ if a quadratic potential function is assumed. The energy levels are equidistant [(a) of fig. 28], and the vibration is said to be 'harmonic'. If, however, higher-order terms are added to the squared term in the potential function, the energy levels converge [(b) of fig. 28]. Instead of 3 overlapping lines (a) we may observe 4 lines of decreasing intensity. The intensity decreases because the population of molecules in excited states rapidly decreases with increasing energy. Usually, therefore, only ν_1 (and, in some cases, also ν_2)

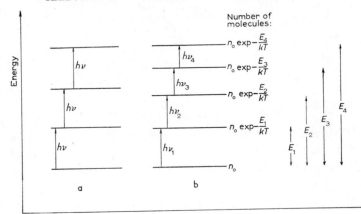

Fig. 28. Showing energy levels of harmonic (a) and anharmonic (b) oscillator. The number of molecules in the excited level, n, obey the rule
$$n = n_0 \exp -E_n/kT.$$

is observed. The vibration is spoken of as 'anharmonic'.

In this way one may explain the lines at 520 and 821 cm^{-1}. Another effect of the 'anharmonicity' is that the selection rules are changed so that n_i may change by more than one unit, giving rise to 'overtones' like $2\nu_1$ and $2\nu_3$. Furthermore, the change in one quantum number does not exclude that another quantum number may change simultaneously by either a positive or negative amount. This explains the presence of 'combination bands', such as $\nu_1 + \nu_3$, $\nu_5 - \nu_1$ etc.

Generally, the $3N-6$ normal vibrations correspond to the *strong* bands of the absorption spectrum, but the rule is difficult to apply as it is certainly not without exceptions.

Important new features enter the picture in the case of *molecules with symmetry properties*. For such molecules, the number of *different* normal vibrational frequencies may be less than $3N-6$, and the number of normal vibrational frequencies which appear in the spectrum may be even smaller.

As example of this, let us consider the linear symmetric molecule CO_2. The number of normal vibrational frequencies expected is $3N-5 = 4$. The four normal vibrations necessary for a description of a random vibration are pictured in fig. 29.

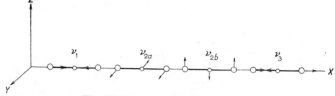

Fig. 29. Normal vibrations of CO_2.

Obviously, the normal vibrations 2a and 2b must take place with the same frequency. Therefore, only three *different* normal vibrational frequencies exist. Vibrations like 2a and 2b are called doubly-degenerate.

We now come to the question of whether these three different normal vibrational frequencies are all *observable*. If the infrared absorption spectrum of CO_2 is studied, only *two* strong bands (at 667 and 2349 cm⁻¹) are found. Obviously, some selection rule is at work.

The dipole moment of unsymmetrical molecules always differs from zero. During all the normal vibrations it changes periodically. Electromagnetic radiation of the normal vibrational frequencies can, therefore, be absorbed (and emitted). All the normal vibrations are 'infrared active'.

A molecule with symmetry properties may possess a dipole moment or not. If the dipole moment differs from zero it might at first be supposed that all the normal vibrations are 'infrared active'.

However, this is not so because of the symmetry. Fig. 18, page 53, shows one of the normal vibrations of CCl_3CH_3. This molecule has a dipole moment, but it does not change during the indicated normal vibration.

CO_2 is a molecule with no permanent dipole moment. However, in the normal vibrations ν_2 and ν_3 a variable moment occurs. The vibrations are, therefore, infrared active while ν_1 is 'forbidden'.

Because of the fundamental importance of the symmetry properties it has proved useful to classify the normal vibrations according to the symmetry properties of the molecule at rest (the stereochemical model). In this way the normal vibrations may be divided into so-called symmetry classes. The *totally symmetrical vibrations* are those normal vibrations which take place with conservation of *all* the symmetry properties of the stereochemical model. ν_1 of fig. 29 is totally symmetric while ν_2 and ν_3 are of lower symmetry.

Normal vibrations belonging to the same symmetry class are all either active or inactive. Tables have been prepared from which the number and character of symmetry classes, the number of vibrations in each symmetry class and their possible infrared activity may be read for symmetric molecules of all kinds. They are, for example, given in Herzberg's 'Infrared and Raman Spectra' op. cit. page 68 (tables 35, 36 and 55). No knowledge of the form of the normal vibrations is required, the 'key' to the tables being the symmetry of the stereochemical formula.

The selection rules mentioned above more or less break down for liquids because of the irregular external field from adjacent molecules. For crystals where this field of force may be known because of the regularity of the arrangement of the molecules, a new set of selection rules may be derived.

IV. 5. ROTATIONAL FINE-STRUCTURE OF INFRARED BANDS

So far no mention of the rotational fine-structure of infrared absorption spectra (page 21 fig. 9) has been made. Infrared spectra consist of bands with *centers* which correspond to the transitions without change of rotational energy discussed in sections 2, 3, and 4 of this chapter. The so-called *branches* of the bands correspond to simultaneous changes in rotational and vibrational energy.

The appearance of infrared bands depends on the type of molecule under investigation (linear molecule, symmetric top etc.), but also on the nature of the pure vibrational transition which 'carries' the band. We shall be content to explain what happens in the simple case of a linear molecule.

Here, $E'_{rot} = BJ(J+1)$ [(1) page 63]. If the wave-number of the pure vibrational transition is ν'_0 we get

$$\Delta E'_{vib} + \Delta E'_{rot} = \nu'_0 + B'J'(J'+1) - B''J''(J''+1) \,.$$

Quantities from the upper state are marked with a single prime. Since B' and B'' differ only slightly we shall here put $B' = B'' = B$ and write

$$\Delta E'_{vib} + \Delta E'_{rot} = \nu'_0 + B[J'(J'+1) - J''(J''+1)] \,.$$

For a non-degenerate vibration (the linear ones) the selection rule is $J' = J'' \pm 1$. For degenerate vibrations (the bending vibrations) transitions are also allowed for which $J' = J''$. Thus, the following possibilities exist:

$J' = J'' + 1$	$\Delta E'_{vib} + \Delta E'_{rot} = \nu'_0 + 2B(J''+1)$	(R-branch)
$J' = J''$	$\Delta E'_{vib} + \Delta E'_{rot} = \nu'_0$	(Q-branch)
$J' = J'' - 1$	$\Delta E'_{vib} + \Delta E'_{rot} = \nu'_0 - 2BJ''$	(P-branch)

It is seen that the so-called R-branch is a series of lines extending towards *increasing* frequencies while the lines of the P-branch extend towards *decreasing* frequencies. In cases where a Q-branch can be observed this line is frequently termed the *zero-line of the band* or the *band center*.

It should be noted that the rotational fine-structure is only available for gases and only through use of grating instruments in the majority of cases. With prism instruments usually only the unresolved band is obtained.

IV. 6. INFORMATION ON MOLECULAR CONSTITUTION AND THERMODYNAMIC PROPERTIES FROM INFRARED SPECTRA

When the constitution of a compound is investigated by chemical methods, two important steps are the clarification of the succession of the atoms (structural chemistry) and, afterwards, the establishment of their relative spatial positions. Infrared spectroscopy is able to contribute to our knowledge of molecular constitution in both ways.

Experiments with molecules of known structural formulae

have, for instance, revealed that infrared absorption spectra of all compounds with C-H groups have strong bands in the 2800–3400 cm^{-1} region. Moreover, absorption close to the upper limit of this region usually occurs when the carbon atom of the C-H group is triple-bonded to another carbon atom while absorption near 3100 cm^{-1} and 2900 cm^{-1} means, respectively, that the carbon atom is double- and single-bonded. An 'aromatic' C-H group like the one in benzene usually gives rise to absorption near 3100 cm^{-1}. There is a number of similar cases in which infrared spectra give information on structural details. Some of the more important 'group' frequencies are listed in table XVI. They are rather independent of the phase.

TABLE XVI

APPROXIMATE POSITIONS OF 'GROUP FREQUENCIES'
OF INFRARED SPECTRA

Group	Group frequency interval
H—O—	3500–3700
H—N<	3300–3500
H—C≡C—	3300–3400
H—C=C<	3000–3100
H—C (aromatic)	3050–3100
H—C (aliphatic)	2800–3000
H—S—	2550–2650
N≡C—	2200–2300
—C≡C—	2170–2270
O=C<	1700–1850
>C=C<	1550–1650
S=C<	1200
F—C<	1100–1300
Cl—C<	700– 800
Br—C<	500– 600
I—C<	400– 500

A chart can be prepared by means of which infrared data can be 'translated' into structural features. This has been done by several authors. Recent publications by Bellamy* and by Sandorfy and Norman Jones** are adequate sources of data and their proper application.

The whole matter is, however, greatly complicated by the fact that infrared spectra do not consist solely of 'group' frequencies. If we consider, say, 1-bromo and 2-bromo propane, easily predicted group frequencies for both molecules are expected at 2800–3000 (CH stretching), 1450 (CH_2 and CH_3 deformation), 1375 (CH_3 deformation), and 500–600 cm^{-1} (CBr stretching), and perhaps a few more. However, we expect a total of $3N - 6 = 27$ normal vibrational frequencies *plus* combination- and over-tones. The spectra of the two compounds will, therefore, differ because of the presence of some 20 normal vibrations that are *not* group frequencies. Their presence may, indeed, make it a matter of considerable difficulty to state whether e.g. absorption found near 550 is really due to a C-Br group and not to something else. Often, therefore, conclusions of a negative character are far more safe. If, for example, a compound of unknown constitution is investigated and no absorption is found in the 400–700 cm^{-1} region, it may be concluded that no C-Br group is present.

Reference to the fact that molecules with identical groups have certain absorption frequencies in common may be made by speaking of the 'group' character of the spectrum. The strong dependence of the infrared spectrum on the chemical structure of the molecule as a whole may be referred to by speaking of the 'structural' character of the spectrum. Because of this distinction one can express the different character of microwave, infrared and visible-ultraviolet spectra as in fig. 30.

* L. J. Bellamy, *The Infra-Red Spectra of Complex Molecules* (John Wiley and Sons, New York, 1958).
** R. Norman Jones and C. Sandorfy, *Application of Infrared and Raman Spectrometry to the Elucidation of Molecular Structure*, in *Chemical Applications of Spectroscopy* in *Technique of Organic Chemistry*, Vol. ix (Interscience Publishers, New York, 1956).

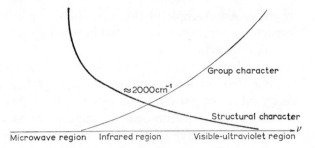

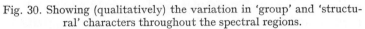

Fig. 30. Showing (qualitatively) the variation in 'group' and 'structural' characters throughout the spectral regions.

Microwave spectra have no group character at all but are extremely sensitive to structural changes. *Infrared spectra* have a pronounced group character above 1300 cm^{-1} but less so below 1300 cm^{-1} where structural influences are great. *Visible-ultraviolet spectra* may be rather poor 'fingerprints', but generally they show excellent group character.

Low resolution infrared spectra give only information on stereoformulae of molecules with symmetry properties. For molecular models of different symmetry, different selection rules apply, resulting in different appearances of the spectra. In this way, the presence of a center of symmetry, planes of symmetry, one or more symmetry axes etc., may be demonstrated. No information on the actual bond lengths and angles is obtained except in cases where the angles follow from the symmetry, as in benzene ($\angle$ CCC $= 120°$) and CH$_4$ ($\angle$ HCH $= 109°28'$).

Indirectly, of course, infrared spectra throw light upon the structure of all molecules. For example, since the methyl group has a threefold axis in molecules like CH$_4$, CH$_3$CH$_3$, CH$_3$CCl$_3$ etc. there is but little doubt that the same is true for all CH$_3$-groups whether they are located in molecules with symmetry properties or not.

Statements on the actual magnitude of bond lengths and valence angles have sometimes been made in cases where the values of the force-constants were believed to be known with some accuracy. An example of this was quoted on page 86 (H_2O). Structural parameters calculated in this way generally are of very limited value.

This picture changes sharply if attention is focussed on the rotational fine-structure of the infrared bands experimentally available by means of grating instruments. Within this field more or less the same features are of importance as those described under microwave spectroscopy (principal moments of inertia). For small molecules, results of great precision have been obtained (because of the comparatively large spacing of the rotational levels). In the first place, the rotational fine-structure of a certain band depends in a characteristic way on the symmetry of the pure vibrational transition involved. Fine-structure studies are, therefore, of great help in getting a reliable interpretation of the spectrum (distinction between normal vibrations of different symmetry, between fundamental and combination bands etc.).

Secondly, bond lengths and angles can be determined with fair accuracy. This part of infrared spectroscopy is, of course, subject to hard competition from microwave spectra, but in a very great number of cases the two methods are supplementary rather than alternative.

As already stated (page 82), electronic structure parameters, although deeply involved in the whole matter, have had to give way to the far less satisfactory force-constants in equations where the measured absorption frequencies are used for quantitative purposes (like the equations on page 86). It is, therefore, up to future theorists and experimenters to translate the 'force-constant language' into an 'electronic-distribution language'.

In spite of its imperfection, the present 'force-constant language' is by no means useless. To mention a few results, it has consistently been found that 'stretching' constants are tenfold larger than 'deformation' constants (p. 86). This almost certainly shows that molecules dissociate by 'breaking', not by stretching. Indeed, the great stability of most diatomic molecules may be considered as being 'due' to the fact that they have no deformation vibration.

In a great number of cases the observation by the chemist of the same bond-type (like multiple bonds, etc.) in various compounds has been strikingly confirmed. Thus, the force-constants of the C–N bonds in HCN, ClCN, BrCN, ICN, and $(CN)_2$ are, respectively, 17.9, 16.7, 16.9, 16.7, and 17.6 in units of 10^5 dynes cm^{-1}. The naive chemical picture of the carbon-carbon single, double, and triple bond is reflected in the force-constants found for the C–C bond in ethane (4.50), ethylene (9.57), and acetylene (15.6) in units of 10^5 dynes cm^{-1}. The factor

$$\prod_1^{3N-6} (1 - e^{-h\nu_i/kT})^{-d_i}$$

which is of importance in the calculation of thermodynamic properties (see the equation on page 79) can be computed by means of a complete set of normal vibrational frequencies since ν_i is one of those frequencies. All of the normal vibrations may, of course, not be found in the infrared spectrum, but in such cases the missing normal vibrational frequencies may frequently be taken from the *Raman spectrum* (page 105). There are, however, cases in which a few of the normal vibrations are 'forbidden' both in infrared absorption and in the Raman effect.

d_i is the degree of degeneracy of the vibration concerned. The occurrence of degenerate vibrations is due to molecular symmetry [for CO_2, the linearity of the molecule (page 92)], and may be predicted by means of symmetry considerations. In cases where this degeneracy can be removed by isotopic substitution, as, for example, in NH_3, where the introduction of one deuterium atom destroys the threefold axis of symmetry, the degree of degeneracy may be found experimentally by investigating if a spectral line in the spectrum of the symmetric compound is merely shifted in frequency because of the isotopic substitution, or whether it is replaced by two or three new lines.

Tables of $[1-\exp(-h\nu_i/kT)]^{-a_i}$ have been worked out by several authors*.

The kind of information on molecular properties obtained from infrared spectra is likewise available from studies of the so-called *Raman spectra*. The experimental conditions under which these spectra are obtained differ, however, considerably from infrared technique. Raman spectra will, therefore, be discussed separately on pages 105–109 (chapter v).

* E. Miller, K. West, and H. J. Bernstein, *Tables of Functions for the Vibrational Contributions to Thermodynamic Quantities* (Nat. Research Council Bull. 1, Ottawa, 1951).

CHAPTER V

SPECTRA OF THE VISIBLE-ULTRAVIOLET REGION

V. 1. RESEARCH POSSIBILITIES

Spectroscopy in the visible region (7000–4000 Å) was the branch of spectroscopy first taken up by investigators, undoubtedly because the human eye could be used as a detector. Research in the ultraviolet region (4000–1000 Å) came as a natural extension since the photographic plate could then be used as the detector in both regions with spectrographs differing only slightly in their general design.

Three different types of molecular spectra have here proved to be of universal applicability: Raman spectra (emission), fluorescence spectra (emission), and 'ordinary' absorption spectra. Spectrographs are commercially available for all three kinds of investigation.

Independent of the state of aggregation, spectra of all three types may be taken, although spectra of crystals and Raman spectra of gases are only rarely reported. The selection rules do not exclude spectral activity of any spectral type; this is true even for homonuclear diatomic molecules.

The spectroscopic resolving power obtainable is satisfactory for most types of research. It may be as high as 300 000 for grating instruments. As a rule, a given resolving power is 'cheaper' here than in the infrared. This great advantage, although of considerable value in a number of interesting cases, is, however, more than counterbalanced by the fact that fluorescence emission spectra and visible-ultraviolet absorption spectra are often more or less *continuous* even if studied

101

for substances in the dilute gas phase. Another disadvantage is that emission and absorption curves of different compounds are often very similar. These phenomena (to be discussed) naturally make it difficult to identify molecules by means of these spectra, and the analysis of mixtures is impossible in many cases. Correspondingly, it is difficult to draw theoretical conclusions from such spectra.

As emphasized, these objections do not apply to the Raman spectra which are discontinuous. In all three cases, however, chemical changes in the sample may occur because of the magnitude of the radiation quanta.

V. 2. DISTINCTION BETWEEN VARIOUS SPECTRAL TYPES

Fig. 31 (page 103) demonstrates the probable mechanisms by which Raman spectra, fluorescence spectra, and visible-ultraviolet absorption spectra arise. Above the ground level (at the bottom) two vibrational excited levels are shown at 400 and 1000 cm^{-1}. Other vibrational levels and all rotational levels are omitted for the sake of simplicity. At the top, one electronically excited level and two electronically *and* vibrationally excited levels are shown. All these *stationary states*, in which the molecules may stay for a brief period (10^{-9} sec), are drawn in full.

When the molecules are irradiated by a monochromatic source which gives radiation with wave-number *insufficient* to excite the molecules electronically (in fig. 31, 26000 cm^{-1}), the collision between light quantum and molecule may be either *'elastic'*, which means that the light quantum is just scattered without change in frequency (*Rayleigh* scattering), or *inelastic*, in which case one of the partners gives up energy to the other. If the *molecule* receives energy, radiation of frequency smaller than ν_i is scattered, the corresponding spectral lines being the *Raman lines*. If energy is transferred to the light quantum, the so-called *anti-Stokes lines* of Raman spectra result. This can, of course, only take place if the molecule

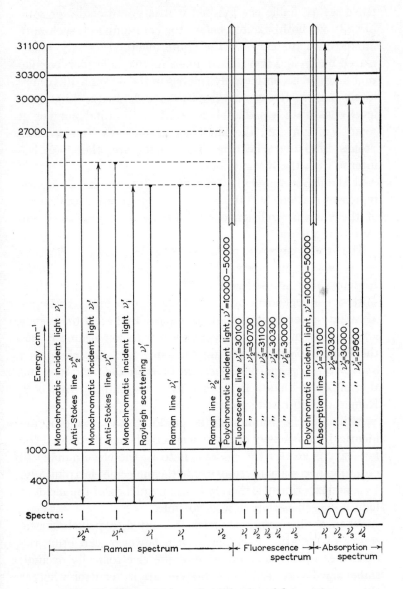

Fig. 31. Different types of visible-ultraviolet spectra.

possesses available energy, i.e., if it is vibrationally or rotationally (or both) excited before the collision. Two such anti-Stokes lines are shown in the figure together with the undisplaced line v_i and two Raman lines. As the molecular 'population density' is considerably smaller in the 400 and 1000 cm^{-1} levels than in the ground level (molecules in the 1000 cm^{-1} level constitute less than 1 per cent of the total number at room temperature), the kind of collisions resulting in anti-Stokes lines must be rare. These lines are, therefore, less intense than the Raman lines.

It should be noted that the dotted lines of fig. 31 do *not* represent stationary states. They merely represent the energy of the various 'collision complexes' between molecules and radiation quanta.

The total number of observable frequency *differences* $v_i - v_1$, $v_i - v_2$, etc. are called the *Raman shifts*. In fig. 31 the Raman shifts are 400 and 1000 cm^{-1}. It is seen that these shifts are independent of v_i. If another monochromatic source of radiation for excitation of the molecules is used (frequency v_j), the spectrum is displaced to another region around v_j, but the Raman *shifts* will remain the same, viz., the *vibrational and rotational quanta of the molecule in its ground state*. Information on these quanta may, therefore, be obtained from both Raman and infrared spectra.

Although the Raman shifts produced by v_i and v_j are identical the *intensity* of the two spectra is not the same. The intensity is greater the closer v_i is to v_e, the wave-number of radiation necessary to really excite the molecule electronically. In some experiments, therefore, the frequency of the incident light is chosen as close to v_e as possible.

When a *fluorescence spectrum* is wanted, a polychromatic source of radiation is chosen which, however, can bring the molecules up into one or more of the electronically excited, *stationary* levels. Experimental conditions control whether the molecule drops from the same level to the bottom levels or from lower-lying, though still electronically excited, levels.

Clearly, information on both the top and the bottom levels is obtained. In several cases it has proved possible to choose a monochromatic source of radiation where the light quanta are of the same magnitude as the difference between two molecular energy levels. If the pressure is kept low so that collisions are rare, one may increase the 'population density' in a particular electronically excited level considerably. When the molecules return to their original state or adjacent states a type of emission spectrum known as 'resonance' spectrum is obtained.

Only low-lying levels which are not too thinly populated play a role in the underlying mechanism of a *visible-ultraviolet absorption spectrum*.

V. 3. RAMAN SPECTRA

It has already been stated (page 104) that the Raman shifts are vibrational and rotational quanta of the molecules in their ground electronic state. If for the moment all molecules with symmetry properties are excluded from the discussion, one might assume that a list of observed Raman shifts of a certain compound would be the same as a list of its observed infrared absorption frequencies. Experience shows, however, that this is only true to a certain approximation. The deviation of the two spectra is, of course, due to the different manners in which they arise.

In the case of infrared absorption, we can think of the molecule as a vibrating classical dipole (frequency v_n) which is able to absorb and emit electromagnetic radiation of the same frequency v_n. No *permanent* electric dipole is necessary to account for infrared activity, since a varying moment may be induced by one or more of the normal vibrations. A homonuclear diatomic molecule shows no infrared activity however, since no dipole moment arises from its normal vibration. Experiments show that such molecules have, however, a Raman spectrum. The reason for this must be of fundamental importance to an understanding of the Raman effect.

In the electric field of the incident radiation a time-dependent dipole moment, μ_i, is induced in the molecule. The electric field vector, F, and μ_i are not parallel except for certain directions of F. For a linear molecule, one of these directions is the molecular axis. Let us, therefore, for the sake of simplicity, assume that F acts in the direction of the axis. We can then write $\mu_i = \alpha_x F$ where α_x is the so-called polarizability in the x-direction (the molecular axis). α_x is, of course, not constant during a normal vibration. To a first approximation we can write:

$$\alpha_x = \alpha_x{}^0 + \alpha_x{}^n \sin 2\pi\nu_n t \ .$$

$\alpha_x{}^0$ is the polarizability in the equilibrium position, $\alpha_x{}^n$ the amplitude of the deviation during the normal vibration of frequency ν_n. As $F = F^0 \sin 2\pi\nu_i t$, where ν_i is the frequency of the incident light, we get

$$\mu_i = \alpha_x{}^0 F^0 \sin 2\pi\nu_i t + \alpha_x{}^n F^0 \sin 2\pi\nu_i t \ \sin 2\pi\nu_n t =$$

$$\underset{\text{Rayleigh line}}{\alpha_x{}^0 F^0 \sin 2\pi\nu_i t} + \underset{\text{Raman line}}{\tfrac{1}{2}\alpha_x{}^n F^0 \cos 2\pi(\nu_i - \nu_n)t} - \underset{\text{Anti-Stokes line.}}{\tfrac{1}{2}\alpha_x{}^n F^0 \cos 2\pi(\nu_i + \nu_n)t}$$

We see that it is $\alpha_x{}^n$, *the change in polarizability during the vibration*, which decides whether there will be Raman lines or not.

As the consideration above can be changed to one of general validity for all molecular types without loss or addition of essential features, we see in the first place that, for all *unsymmetrical molecules*, all $3N - 6$ normal vibrations are 'allowed'. This corresponds to the selection rule

$$\Delta n_i = \pm 1 \quad \text{while} \quad \Delta n_j = 0 \qquad (i \neq j) \ .$$

So far this gives the same set of frequencies as in infrared, but because of the very different underlying mechanism we might easily imagine that the *intensity distribution is very different*. This is not only found as far as the normal vibrations are concerned, but also when one considers the intensities of overtones and combination bands. As a rule, such frequencies are only 0.01 as intense as the 'fundamentals' (the normal vibrations) in Raman spectra, while their intensities in infrared absorption may easily amount to 10–20 per cent of the fundamentals. While it is quite a task to point out the fundamentals from an infrared spectrum, the same problem is generally solved more easily be means of a Raman spectrum.

Secondly, if *molecules with symmetry properties* are considered, the difference in underlying mechanisms between Raman and infrared spectra explains why the selection rules are quite different in the two cases. The normal vibration of homonuclear diatomic molecules was a striking example of this. Let us consider also the normal vibrations of CO_2, fig. 29, page 92.

Here, it may readily be seen that there is a considerable change of polarizability during ν_1 (which must, therefore, be Raman active). For ν_3 it is seen that what is gained in polarizability at one end of the molecule is simultaneously lost at the other end, so that this vibration is *inactive* in the Raman effect. If we consider ν_2 we find it difficult to guess the answer. To a first approximation the vibration does not result in changes in inter-atomic distances. This suggests that ν_2 is probably not Raman active. Actually, this is correct, but the example demonstrates that rules for activity in the Raman effect are usually more difficult to derive from normal vibration pictures than corresponding rules for spectral activity in the infrared. However, the tables in Herzberg's 'Infrared and Raman Spectra' (loc. cit. page 93), which are used for infrared spectra, include the rules for Raman spectra, too. One of the rules says that for a molecule with a center of symmetry, lines that are allowed in infrared are forbidden in Raman effect and vice versa. The converse of the rule, that infrared *in*active bands are always allowed in Raman effect and vice versa, does not follow since normal vibrations exist which are inactive in both types of spectra.

Usually, therefore, infrared and Raman spectra supplement each other in a very important way.

On the whole, Raman spectra may serve as a source of information on valence forces, molecular constitution and thermodynamic properties in much the same way as infrared spectra. Table XVI, page 95, is valid here too. Thus, Raman spectra have the same 'group' and 'structural' character as infrared spectra, i.e., stereoformulae of molecules with symmetry properties may be verified or refuted and force-constants can be calculated. The vast literature on rotational fine-structure of infrared bands has, however, almost no parallel in Raman effect. The reason is, of course, that such experiments must take place *using substances in their gas phase* (where the intensity will be small). Work of this kind by means of a suitable technique has mainly been concentrated on obtaining the 'pure' rotational Raman spectrum which is situated very close to the exciting line. Pure rotational transitions which cannot be studied by means of the microwave technique because of the absence of molecular dipole moment, have been found in this way for molecules with small moments of inertia, such as H_2, D_2, N_2 and O_2. Work by *Stoicheff* includes studies of larger molecules such as butatriene, benzene, etc.*.

There are two important experimental reasons in favour of carrying out infrared and not Raman measurements if a choice must be made.

1. Infrared spectra of substances in all three states of aggregation may be taken comparatively easily. Raman spectra of solids and gases are more difficult to get at present.

2. If the infrared spectrum of a sample, consisting of pure compound and impurities, is obtained, the spectrum is to a good approximation a superposition of the spectra of the individual compounds.

While the same may be true for a Raman spectrum, the difficulty exists that one of the impurities may have a low-lying, electronically excited level, and may, therefore, start to fluoresce. The entire spectrum may be ruined in this way,

* B. P. Stoicheff, *High Resolution Raman Spectroscopy*, in *Advances in Spectroscopy*, Vol. I, page 91 (Interscience Publishers Inc., New York, 1959).

because the (generally continuous) fluorescence is far stronger than the weak Raman lines. These impurities may, of course, be removed, but often only at considerable cost of labour and material. Thus, the separation of the compound(s) of interest from its (their) impurities is a far more decisive factor in Raman work than in infrared studies.

As mentioned on page 6, infrared prism spectrographs only cover the spectral region from 2 to 40μ, i.e. from 5000–250 cm^{-1} (without TlBrI optics the wave-number range is even restricted to the 5000–400 cm^{-1} interval). Moreover, the *same* prism cannot be used throughout these regions. It is an important feature in favour of carrying out Raman investigations that Raman shifts in the 50–250 cm^{-1} interval are obtained together with the 250–5000 cm^{-1} shifts by means of *one* optical arrangement.

V. 4. ELECTRONIC BAND SPECTRA

Introductory Remarks

Now, let us summarize briefly what we know empirically of the energy of the stationary molecular states from microwave, infrared, and Raman spectra by means of an example. Microwave absorption may have been found at 30000 Mc sec^{-1} (~ 1 cm^{-1}), infrared absorption at 300, 417,..., 9120 cm^{-1} and Raman shifts at 417,..., 3050 cm^{-1}. Based on this we can sketch a diagram like fig. 32.

In the diagram it has been assumed that the vibrational quanta were absorbed by molecules in the vibrational ground level. Experimentally we can be sure of this by cooling the sample sufficiently. We now irradiate with visible-ultraviolet light. Suppose that the first absorption found by gradually increasing the wave-number from 10000 cm^{-1} (10000 Å) on is at 30000 cm^{-1} (3333 Å). This would be a typical example.

It is seen that the spectroscopic methods hitherto dealt with do not inform us on the possible energy levels in the

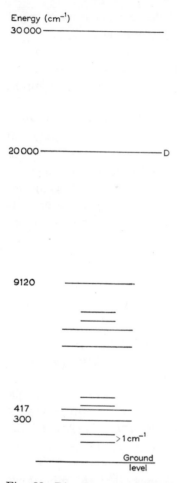

Fig. 32. Diagram of empirical spectral data.

gap between 9120 and 30000 cm⁻¹. The problem, therefore, arises: what happens to the molecule in this broad interval? 20000 cm⁻¹ is about 56 kcal per mole. We have labelled this level with a D because this energy is sufficient to *dissociate* many molecules. The particles in the state at 30000 cm⁻¹ cannot, therefore, be the original molecules, but they must either be dissociation products or some isomeric form of the molecules from the ground level. If the first alternative can be excluded, the 'isomerism' obviously can be explained as a difference in electronic distribution in analogy to what happens when *atoms* absorb quanta of this magnitude. A survey of these relations for *diatomic molecules* is usually given as a diagram like fig. 33.

The lower curve of fig. 33 is the potential curve for the molecule in its ground state. The atoms are brought together from infinity to distances smaller than r_e'' *with zero velocity*. As the total energy is the sum of potential and kinetic energy, the curves are potential energy curves. The vibrational levels are shown as horizontal lines; the rotational levels are omitted. If we think of the molecule in a classical way it is at rest at a and b (to take an example). Here, its energy is purely potential, E, while the points on

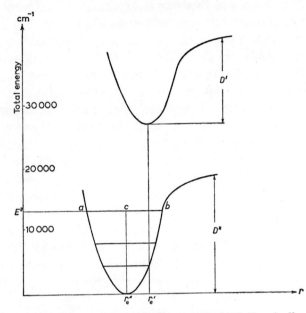

Fig. 33. Showing potential curves for ground and electronically excited states of diatomic molecule. r_e = equilibrium distance, D = dissociation energy.

the horizontal line between a and b represent situations with both potential and kinetic energy, except at c where the energy is purely kinetic. The molecule can, therefore, be thought of as carrying out oscillations between a and b.

The upper part of fig. 33 shows corresponding features. The electronically excited molecule is considered as having vibrational and rotational levels (not shown), an equilibrium distance r_e', etc.

A picture like fig. 33 goes, of course, far beyond what can be concluded from the empirical data of fig. 32. But we shall see that many features of electronic band spectra can be understood within this framework.

In trying to explain why the vibrational levels in the 10 000–20 000 cm⁻¹ interval cannot be studied by means of infrared or Raman methods we must refer to the selection rule $\Delta n_i = 1$, perhaps extended to permit changes of 2 or 3. A transition from the ground state to, say, $15\,000$ cm^{-1}, would have to take place in about five successive steps of 3000 cm^{-1}. As long as temperature equilibrium is maintained, such a process is highly improbable. An adequate raising of the temperature in order to 'populate' vibrationally excited levels is out of question (20–$30\,000°$ would be needed). However, as we shall see, information on these highly excited vibrational levels of the electronic ground state is accessible through studies of visible-ultraviolet emission spectra, since molecules from upper electronic states may drop to these levels.

The advantage of studying visible-ultraviolet spectra is, therefore, partly, that in this way single molecules may be 'heated' to $50\,000$–$100\,000°$ by a radiation 'injection'. Important information on the molecules in their electronically excited levels, and also in their (electronic) ground level, hereby becomes available.

As soon as the molecule has N atoms the potential function is a $3N-6$ dimensional hypersurface. Such functions are hard to visualize. This is one of the reasons why diatomic molecules are used as examples in the following. We shall draw attention to the differences if polyatomic molecules are considered.

V. 5. ELECTRONIC ENERGY LEVELS AND SELECTION RULES

If the minimum energy of the potential function of a molecule is denoted by E_{el}, we can obviously write:

$$E_{tot} = E_{el} + E_{vib} + E_{rot}.$$

The appearance of the electronic spectra now depends on the selection rules and the sharpness of the energy levels.

Finite expressions for E_{el} cannot be given. The problem of calculating the permitted values of the electronic energy is complicated, even for diatomic molecules. A comprehensive

review of the various methods to apply has been given by
C. A. Coulson*. However, even without any knowledge of
the energies of electronically excited states these states may
nevertheless be characterized by certain quantum numbers
e.g. those referring to the orbital angular momentum and the
spin of the electrons.

For *diatomic* molecules we can write:

$$E_{\text{vib}} = h\nu(n + \tfrac{1}{2}), \qquad E_{\text{rot}} = hcBJ(J + 1).$$

The effects of anharmonicity and centrifugal stretching have
been ignored for simplicity.

If quantities referring to the upper electronic state are
marked with single prime, quantities from the lower state
with double prime, the energy differences between upper and
lower levels for diatomic molecules are:

$$\Delta E = \Delta E_{\text{el}} + h[\nu'(n' + \tfrac{1}{2}) - \nu''(n'' + \tfrac{1}{2})] + \\ + hc[B'J'(J' + 1) - B''J''(J'' + 1)].$$

We shall successively discuss the selection rules for the electronic quantum numbers, for the vibrational quantum numbers (n' and n''), and for the rotational quantum numbers, J'
and J''.

Selection Rules for the Electronic Quantum Numbers

Most molecules have a series of electronically excited
'isomers'. In part, they may be distinguished from each other
as follows in the case of *diatomic molecules*:

The electrons move in a field of axial symmetry, the symmetry axis being the molecular axis. With reference to fig. 34
we now form the sum $M = \Sigma \mu v_i r_i$. According to quantum
mechanics this quantity, M, which is the axial component
of the total angular momentum of the electrons in their orbital movement, can only take on the values $(h/2\pi)\Lambda$ where
$\Lambda = 0, 1, 2, 3$ etc. The corresponding states are labelled Σ, Π,
Δ, Φ, respectively. It should be noted that the *energy* of the

* C. A. Coulson, *Valence* (Clarendon Press, Oxford, 1952).

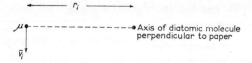

Fig. 34. Showing axis of diatomic molecule, an electron (mass μ), and its distance to the axis (r_i) together with its velocity component $\bar{v}_i$ perpendicular to r_i in the plane of the paper.

electronic states is not a single-valued function of Λ. Two energetically very different states may not differ in Λ-value (but they may, in a general way, be thought of as differing in average electronic distance from the axis). Nevertheless, Λ is useful for the formulation of the selection rules since it can be shown that only transitions for which $\Delta\Lambda = 0$ or ± 1 can appear in absorption and emission.

In addition to an 'orbital' velocity each electron possesses a certain 'spin' angular momentum, $\frac{1}{2}h/2\pi$. This spin has, of course, directional properties so that it must be represented by a vector, s_i. The quantity that matters for the interaction between radiation and matter is, however, not the single s_i's, but their vector sum S. Generally, S is a small quantity, $\frac{1}{2}$, 1, $\frac{3}{2}$,... in units of $h/2\pi$, since most of the electrons are 'paired' so as to give no contribution to S. In our symbols for electronic states, the magnitude of S enters in the form of $2S + 1$ which is placed at the upper left corner of the Λ-symbol. For the state $^1\Sigma$, $\Lambda = 0$ and $S = 0$. The $^3\Pi$-state has $\Lambda = 1$ and $S = 1$, etc. The selection rule for S is: $\Delta S = 0$.

For *polyatomic molecules*, the selection rule $\Delta S = 0$ is maintained. Other rules replace the Λ-rule. Λ is the electronic angular momentum component along the axis which is the only *symmetry element* of the diatomic molecule. For polyatomic molecules the possible presence of other symmetry properties decides how the whole matter has to be discussed. As even a short introduction to this field is completely beyond the scope of this book, the reader is referred to an article by H. Sponer and E. Teller* for further information.

---

* H. Sponer and E. Teller, *Reviews of Modern Physics 13*, 75 (1941).

Selection Rules for the Vibrational Quantum Numbers

When an attempt is made to interpret electronic band spectra of diatomic molecules, it becomes clear that no consistent set of selection rules as simple as, for example, the rule $\Delta n = 1$ for infrared and Raman spectra, exists. For some of the transitions of one molecule the rule seems to be $\Delta n = 4$ or 5; for the transitions of another molecule the rule may be $\Delta n = 2$, etc. The underlying principle of this apparent inconsistency in selection rules was explained by J. Franck in terms of the classical theory and discussed more completely by E. U. Condon in the quantum theory.

According to the *Franck-Condon principle*, transitions from the vibrational levels of one electronic state to the vibrational levels of another electronic state which are active spectroscopically take place before the *nuclei* can alter their positions and velocities.

Franck's explanation involved regarding the molecule as oscillating classically between (a) and (b) (see fig. 33). Condon 'translated' this to the more correct language of quantum-mechanics, but, since the results are essentially the same, we shall for the present discussion use the classical representation.

Fig. 35 shows three typical examples. Let us first examine how the vibrational selection rules for visible-ultraviolet *absorption* spectra can be found by means of the Franck-Condon principle. Here, it is essential to remember that most of the molecules are in the lowest vibrational states. In case (a) it is seen that the only transitions consistent with the principle are the ones for which $\Delta n = 0$, 1, or 2. Transitions to higher levels would mean a larger change in either position or velocity or both. However, at the potential curve the velocity of the oscillating molecule is always zero, so that transitions can take place between points situated vertically above each other, as indicated by the arrows pointing upwards, in (a). Likewise, in (b) the rule becomes $\Delta n = 3$, 4 and 5. In (c), the region around the limit between discrete and continuous energy states (dotted line) is hit by the vertical lines from the $n'' = 0$ level.

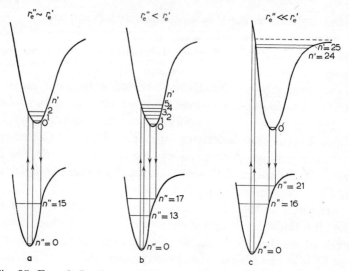

Fig. 35. Franck-Condon parabolae. (a), (b), and (c) represent cases of increasing difference between the equilibrium distance in the electronically excited state and the ground level.

In this case we expect a series of discrete lines, corresponding to the rule $\Delta n = 24$ and 25, joining on to a region of continuous absorption. This is one of the ways in which partly continuous absorption spectra may arise (for further ways, see predissociation, page 118).

If an *emission experiment* is arranged by, for example, placing the diatomic molecule in a discharge tube the distribution of the molecules among the upper states is a function of pressure, voltage, etc. Under conditions where the molecules are concentrated in the $n' = 0$ level (low voltage, high pressure), the selection rules will be: $\Delta n = 15$; $\Delta n = 13$ and 17; $\Delta n = 16$ and 21, respectively, in the cases (a), (b), and (c).

In a *fluorescence experiment*, where the excitation is performed by irradiation, the states $n' = 0$, 1 and 2; $n' = 3$, 4 and 5; $n' = 24$ and 25 may be enriched with molecules. Transitions to the ground state levels may take place from these levels if the pressure is sufficiently low. This, of course, results in still other selection rules which may differ radically from the rules that are valid for experiments in the discharge tube.

For *polyatomic* molecules the vibrational selection rules are somewhat more inexact. We have here $3N - 6$ normal vibrations. The extension of the Franck-Condon principle to polyatomic molecules means (to a first approximation) that the totally symmetric vibrations are the only ones for which Δn deviates from zero. For all other transitions, to a first approximation, $\Delta n = 0$. These rules mean a very considerable simplification of the vibrational features of electronic band spectra compared to what one might have expected at first thought.

Selection Rules for the Rotational Quantum Number Electronic Band Fine-Structure

For *diatomic* molecules the selection rules for J are: $\Delta J = 0$ or ± 1. The only exception to this rule occurs if the transition takes place between two Σ-states. Then $\Delta J = 0$ is forbidden.

Setting $\Delta E_{el} + hc[v'(n' + \frac{1}{2}) - v''(n'' + \frac{1}{2})] = hcv_0'$, we get

$J' = J'' + 1$ (the R-branch):

$$E = hcv_0' + hc[B'(J'' + 1)(J'' + 2) - B''J''(J'' + 1)] \, ,$$

$J' = J''$ (the Q-branch):

$$E = hcv_0' + hcJ''(J'' + 1)(B' - B'') \, ,$$

$J' = J'' - 1$ (the P-branch):

$$E = hcv_0' + hc[B'(J'' - 1)J'' - B''J''(J'' + 1)] \, .$$

A survey of what this means in terms of the spectrum can be obtained by remembering that in most cases B' is only slightly smaller than B'' (corresponding to $r_e' > r_e''$). It is now easy to see that the Q-branch is a series of very closely spaced lines at the low-frequency side of v_0 due to the smallness of $B'' - B'$. The R-branch must have a much larger spacing between its lines which must come on the high frequency side of v_0. The P-branch also has lines with large spacing (compared to the Q-branch), and the lines fall on the low-frequency side of v_0, which is called the *zero-line* of the band. In this way it has been possible to explain the main features of the fine-structure of electronic band spectra of diatomic molecules. The fine-structure of electronic bands is, of course, quite analogous to the fine-structure of infrared bands (page 93).

For *polyatomic* molecules, the fine-structure may, of course, be extremely difficult to analyze. In the general case of an asymmetric top *six* different moments of inertia enter the considerations since the rotational constants A, B, and C may differ considerably in the two electronic states. The selection rule for J is still as simple as for diatomic molecules, but because of the inherent complexity of the problem only a few simple molecules have been studied in detail (e.g. formaldehyde).

In a great many cases the electronic spectra do not even possess rotational fine-structure but prove to be continuous even if studied in the dilute gas phase. This is due to the phenomenon of predissociation.

Predissociation

If a diatomic molecule in its electronic, vibrational and rotationless ground level is supplied with the dissociation energy D, the molecule may split into two atoms at rest. If the increase in energy is greater than D, the molecule may split into the same two atoms, but this time they will not be at rest since the energy in excess of D becomes translational energy. This translational energy can adopt a continuous range of values so that the area above the potential curve is called the *dissociation continuum*. The mutual positions of the potential surfaces (curves) of a molecule in its ground state and in its electronically excited states are such that the discrete energy states of the upper curve are at a level with the dissociation continuum of the lower state.

Quantum mechanics shows that when the discrete states to be expected for an atomic or molecular system and a dissociation continuum of the same system (molecule) are at the same level then there is a chance that the expected discrete levels are more or less diffuse. When the levels *are* diffuse, radiationless transitions take place from these levels to the continuum. This phenomenon has been observed for atomic spectra where it is called the *Auger effect*. Its importance for the visible-ultraviolet spectra of polyatomic molecules is very much greater. The potential function of one electronic state usually 'dips' into the dissociation continuum of a lower state, in which case the normal discrete levels of the higher state may become diffuse. Moreover, the potential hypersurface of the ground electronic state has 'towers' of discrete energy levels, corresponding to normal vibrations of high frequency, reaching far up into the dissociation continua for normal vibrations of low frequency, so that electronic excitation is not a neccessary condition for the effect to occur. Undoubtedly, this phenomenon represents a very serious limitation to what may be learned from electronic spectra since, as a consequence, the spectra frequently become diffuse or continuous. Its occurrence may, of course, sometimes yield useful information on the relative positions of the potential surfaces.

V. 6. INFORMATION ON MOLECULAR CONSTITUTION AND THERMODYNAMIC PROPERTIES FROM ELECTRONIC BAND SPECTRA

By far the most popular use of electronic spectra is made in the form of experimental determinations of absorption curves of liquids as such, or of liquids and solids dissolved in transparent media.

In all these cases the rotational fine-structure is lost because of the great molecular density. The same is partly true for the vibrational detail. Therefore, spectrographs of moderate resolving power are adequate for such studies.

For a *parallel* beam of *monochromatic* light, the change in light intensity, dI, per cm, dI/dx, is proportional to the radiation intensity, I, at the point considered:

$$-\frac{dI}{dx} = \alpha I \qquad \text{Integration gives:} \qquad I_x = I_0^0 e^{-\alpha x}.$$

This is *Lambert's law*. $I_0{}^0$ is the intensity of the incident light, I_x the intensity at path-length x and α is the so-called *absorption coefficient*. So far, no regard has been taken to the presence of the cell windows. It is easy to show, however, that if I_0 is the intensity of the light passing the empty sample container and I the intensity of the light passing the cell *with* sample then

$$I = I_0 e^{-\alpha x}$$

which is usually formulated as

$$I = I_0 \, 10^{-D}$$

where D is the *optical density*, mentioned on page 9. A curve, representing D as a function of wave-length, is primarily desired as the result of an experiment.

For solutions, liquids, and gases one can write $D = \varepsilon c x$ where c is the molar concentration of absorbing, *identical* molecules. This last point must be emphasized, for in the case of solutions, the absorbing molecules may not be identical with the ones that were originally dissolved. Dissociation or association may occur so that the absorption curve is partly due to unchanged molecules, partly to dissociation and association products (complex compounds formed from solvent and solute). This facilitates understanding that the law

$$I = I_0 \, 10^{-\varepsilon c x} \qquad \cdot$$

often called the *Lambert-Beer* law, is most easily applied for dilute gases and solutions. In a dilute solution a possible effect of complex formation between solute and solvent is at its maximum. The ε of the Lambert-Beer law is called *the molar extinction coefficient*.

The wide applicability of the above equation for determination of concentrations is self-evident. Of course, the equation applies to absorption experiments in all spectral regions, but it should be noted when spectrographs of higher resolving power are used for production of discontinuous spectra that the law must be used taking into account several other factors, such as monochromator properties, the width of the absorption line, the presence of foreign gases etc.

Referring now in the following solely to extinction curves of unmixed molecules, quite a few relationships between chemical formula and the main features of the absorption curve have been detected. Some of these relationships were already found by the chemists of the 19th century who realized that the *colour* of a number of different compounds with one group in common – which they called the chromophore – was the same. The spectrographs soon revealed that a great number of such chromophores exist. For example, compounds with a single $C=C$ group all show strong absorption in the 1800–2000 Å region. Compounds with a carboxyl group (and no other chromophore) absorb at 2100 Å; compounds with a single phenyl group have a strong absorption band at 2700 Å; etc. If several of these chromophores are present in the molecule simultaneously the absorption is simply an addition of the effects of the various groups, provided, however, that the chromophores are located sufficiently far from each other in the molecule. Otherwise, especially in the case of 'conjugation', the spectrum changes in a complicated way.

Absorption spectra in the visible-ultraviolet region, therefore, show a great deal of 'group' character without being totally devoid of structural features, but the group character may in many cases be so dominant that it may be dangerous to reason from identity of absorption curves to identity of the substances. For further information the reader is referred to the review article by E. A. Braude* and to the book by Gillam and Stern**.

Beyond what may be revealed by use of the above-mentioned, more or less empirical relationships, electronic band spectra are primary sources of information on molecular elec-

* E. A. Braude, *Ultraviolet Light Absorption and the Structure of Organic Compounds*, Annual Reports of Chem. Society (London) XLII, 105 (1945).
** A. E. Gillam and E. S. Stern, *Electronic Absorption Spectroscopy* (Edward Arnold Publ., London, 1954).

tronic distribution. It is, however, excluded that even a short review of this field can be given within the scope of this book. A proper understanding of the electronic distribution is of more than theoretical interest as it is only through such understanding that the above-mentioned empirical relationships may be interpreted correctly and, subsequently, used with more safety.

Naturally, *quantitative* results have been most numerous in the case of diatomic molecules. Very precise values of dissociation energies have been found. This is important since the combustion technique used for many other molecules offers special difficulties for diatomic compounds. Table XVII gives some of these values taken from the book by Gerhard Herzberg[*], which contains a general treatment of microwave, infrared, Raman and electronic spectra of diatomic molecules[†].

The dissociation energies, D_0^0, of the table are all taken from electronic band spectra. D_0^0 is the energy difference between a state of dissociation into two neutral atoms at rest and the ground level (*not* the hypothetical vibrationless ground state).

The equilibrium distances – which refer to the hypothetical, vibrationless ground state – are taken from electronic band spectra (E), microwave spectra (MW), infrared spectra (I), or Raman spectra (R).

Important quantitative results have also been obtained by the study of spectra of the products of 'flash' photolysis. This work has recently been reviewed by *Ramsay*[**].

Because of the high electronic excitation energy electronic levels are almost never of any importance to calculations of the partition function.

[*] Gerhard Herzberg, *Spectra of Diatomic Molecules* (D. Van Nostrand Co., Inc., New York, 1950).
[†] A bibliography of spectra of diatomic molecules 1950–60 (with addenda and errata) has been prepared by G. Herzberg and L.L. Howe, National Research Council of Canada.
[**] D. A. Ramsay, *The Spectra of Polyatomic Free Radicals*, in *Advances in Spectroscopy*, Vol. I, page 1 (Interscience Publishers Inc., New York, 1959).

TABLE XVII

DISSOCIATION ENERGIES AND EQUILIBRIUM DISTANCES OF DIATOMIC
MOLECULES

Molecule	D_0^0			r_e Å
	Electron volts	cm^{-1}	kcal/mole	
$Ag^{107}I^{127}$	2.98_3	24067	68.797	
$Cl^{35}F^{19}$	2.616	21107	60.333	1.62813 (MW)
$Cl^{35}Cl^{35}$	2.475	19969	57.081	1.988 (E)
$Br^{79}Br^{81}$	1.971	15902	45.457	2.3836 (E)
$Cl^{35}I^{127}$	2.152	17363	49.632	2.32069 (MW)
$Br^{79}I^{127}$	1.817_0	14660	41.905	
$I^{127}I^{127}$	1.5417	12439	35.556	2.666_6 (E)
T_2	4.588_1	37018	105.81	
D_2	4.553_6	36740	105.02	0.7416_4 (R)
HT	4.524_1	36502	104.34	
HD	4.511_2	36398	104.04	0.7413_6 (R)
H_2	4.476_3	36116	103.23	0.7416_6 (R)
DCl^{35}	4.481	36154	103.34	1.274_9 (I)
HCl^{35}	4.430	35743	102.17	1.2746 (I)
HBr	3.75_4	30300	86.600	1.413_8 (I)
HI^{127}	3.0564	24657	70.490	1.604_1 (1)

CHAPTER VI

MAGNETIC RESONANCE SPECTRA

VI. 1. RESEARCH POSSIBILITIES

There are two types of magnetic resonance spectra, nuclear magnetic resonance (NMR-) spectra and electronic magnetic resonance (EMR*-) spectra. Spectroscopic equipment for both types of spectra is commercially available, and a maintenance service, especially necessary for the rather complex nuclear magnetic resonance instrument, has been established. Contrary to what is more or less the case within other branches of spectroscopy, it makes no sense to produce an instrument of low resolving power since the spectroscopic phenomena of greatest interest do not occur unless the spectrograph is a refined and therefore expensive tool.

NMR- and EMR-spectra may be taken of compounds in all three states of aggregation. A *proviso* for taking an NMR-spectrum is, of course, that the molecular species to be investigated contain nuclei with magnetic properties. This is no serious limitation since important nuclei such as H, D, ^{14}N, ^{15}N, ^{19}F, ^{35}Cl, ^{37}Cl, ^{79}Br, ^{81}Br, ^{127}I, ^{31}P, ^{10}B, ^{11}B etc. *are* magnetic. A few important nuclei like ^{12}C, ^{16}O, and ^{32}S are non-magnetic, but this difficulty may be circumvented, if necessary, by application of the magnetic isotopes ^{13}C, ^{17}O, and ^{33}S.

Since all *electrons* are magnetic it would seem that an EMR-spectrum is always obtainable. This is not so because in most molecules electrons are paired in such a way as to 'neutralize' the magnetic property of the single electron. However, some

---

* Very frequently called EPR-spectra in the literature ('electron paramagnetic resonance') or ESR-spectra ('electron spin resonance').

124

molecules *do* contain one or two unpaired electrons ('free radicals', 'bi-radicals') in which case an EMR-spectrum may always be obtained. At first glance this limitation might seem rather unfortunate, but to a great extent this disadvantage is counterbalanced by the fact that free radicals, generally only present in minute concentration in a medium of stable molecules or *in vacuo*, may be detected *selectively* by the EMR-technique, which, in this respect, supplements the highly sensitive visible-ultraviolet spectroscopy in a very important way.

To illustrate the available power of resolution as compared to the range within which spectra occur, it might be mentioned that *proton* magnetic resonance spectra usually fall within a 0.150 oersted* range in an external magnetic field of 15000 oersted. Instruments separating lines only 10^{-4} oersted apart are available. In the EMR-spectrum of the triphenylmethyl radical at 10000 oersted some 70 lines are seen separately within a 30 oersted range. The reason for giving magnetic resonance spectra as a function of magnetic field intensity H instead of frequency will be explained in the next section.

Since in different molecules magnetic nuclei and unpaired electrons are usually in different surroundings (chemical bonds, other magnetic nuclei, etc.), it follows that both NMR- and EMR-spectra have an individual character. As a rule, however, the 'fingerprint' character is more pronounced for NMR-spectra. In addition to what might be learned theoretically from these spectra, NMR-spectra are, therefore, of great use in an analytical respect. Not only can they serve more or less in the way infrared spectra do, for example, but in cases where the components of a mixture contain different nuclei (e.g. CH_3COCl, CF_3COCl) one may successively 'tune in' (to be explained) on different atomic species (H and F in the example), measuring the amount of each component under conditions where the presence of the remaining component(s) play(s) a vanishingly small role.

* Magnetic field intensity unit (for vacuum). 'Gauss' is the magnetic induction unit (for matter).

VI. 2. ENERGETICS AND SELECTION RULES

Particles such as electrons and atomic nuclei possessing a spin have *magnetic* properties, the spinning charge representing a tiny electrical current. The magnetic property is conveniently expressed by the magnetic moment, μ, of the spinning particle. For the electron, with spin vector $s = \frac{1}{2}$, μ_e equals -9270×10^{-24} ergs/oersted. For the proton, with $s = \frac{1}{2}$, μ_H equals 14.1×10^{-24} ergs/oersted. In a homogeneous magnetic field spinning particles orient themselves in certain fixed directions relative to the magnetic field intensity vector H (page 46). If the spin of the particle is I, $2I + 1$ orientations of slightly different energy are possible. If m is the projection of I on H, the $2I + 1$ positions are characterized by $m = I$, $I-1$, $I-2, \ldots, -I+1$, $-I$. The minimum magnetic energy of the particle being $-H|\mu|$ and the maximum being $H|\mu|$, we get that the maximum magnetic energy difference, caused by different orientations in the field, is $2H|\mu|$. Since the positions of extreme energy correspond to $m = \pm I$, and since the energy difference $2H|\mu|$ is divided into $2I$ *equal* portions as a result of changing m, it is seen that the energy difference between successive levels becomes $2H|\mu|/2I$. The selection rule is $\Delta m = \pm 1$, leading to the fundamental equation

$$h\nu_{\exp} = \frac{2H|\mu|}{2I} = \frac{H|\mu|}{I} , \tag{1}$$

connecting the experimentally observable emission or abosrption frequency, $\nu_{\exp}$, with the field intensity, H, of the magnet, the magnetic moment μ of the particle, and its spin I.

Inserting $H = 10000$ oersted, $I = \frac{1}{2}$ (for electrons and protons), and $h = 6.6 \times 10^{-27}$, it is seen that *proton* magnetic resonance spectra ($\mu_H = 14 \times 10^{-24}$) occur at 40 Mc sec^{-1} while EMR-spectra ($\mu_e = -9270 \times 10^{-24}$) are found at 28000 Mc sec^{-1}.

Equation (1) shows H and $\nu_{\exp}$ to be proportional. Most experiments are performed keeping $\nu_{\exp}$ constant and varying H. This is the reason for giving magnetic resonance spectra as functions of H, but for the sake of convenience many authors use cycles/sec as abscissa, thereby obtaining the advantage that abscissa differences multiplied by Planck's constant are converted to energy units. In typical cases of NMR-spectra such differences amount to 1–100 cycles/sec. For EMR-spectra, the differences are about a thousandfold higher.

VI. 3. INTERPRETATION OF NMR-SPECTRA

So far, we have been talking of NMR-spectra without specifying the physical and chemical state of the sample containing the nuclei. If, say, all *protons* absorbed at exactly the same frequency and field intensity, there would be no reason to count NMR-spectra among the disciplines of molecular spectroscopy. Actually, deviations occur according to the physical state of the sample, but, on top of this, even if protons of different molecules are studied under equal physical conditions (e.g. as a dilute solution of molecules in the same solvent), differences still occur. These differences may be given in cycles/sec, in millioersteds etc. It is readily seen that it is convenient to choose a definite reference standard with an absorption line to which all other absorption lines may be referred. The compound most frequently used for this purpose at present is tetramethylsilane, $Si(CH_3)_4$. In many cases, this compound may simply be mixed with the sample investigated without causing chemical or magnetic changes. Cyclohexane, water, and benzene have been used for the same purpose. One advantage of using $Si(CH_3)_4$ is that its resonance occurs at a magnetic field intensity *higher* than that for most other protons. Denoting the resonance field intensity by H_x for the proton being studied, and denoting the (single) proton resonance in $Si(CH_3)_4$ by H_r, we may use the (negative) quantity $H_x - H_r$ as a quantitative indication that somehow the 'x' and the 'r' protons are in a different environment. In a similar way *frequency differences* $\Delta = \Delta_x - \Delta_r$ may be used.

Now, whereas there is a 'theory' for microwave, infrared,

and Raman spectra because the classical picture of rotation and vibration of molecules may be translated so readily into quantum-mechanical language, we meet the same difficulty in 'explaining' NMR- and EMR-spectra as encountered for electronic band spectra. These latter spectral types clearly depend on the motion of the electrons, for which no simple adequate classical picture exists. As a result, it is not feasible here, even if recourse were taken to rather advanced mathematics, to derive equations, for example, relating $H_x - H_r$ to molecular structure. Several regularities exist, but most have been found experimentally. Here, we shall therefore confine ourselves to discussing some of the more important *experimental* results. The theoretical background has been treated by Ramsey and Pople*, among others.

An observation of primary importance is that $H_x - H_r$ is proportional to H. This immediately leads to a definition of the quantity δ:

$$\delta = \frac{H_x - H_r}{H} \sim \frac{H_x - H_r}{H_r} \sim \frac{\Delta(\text{cycles/sec})}{\nu_{\text{exp}}}.$$

δ is called *the chemical shift*. It is independent of the applied magnetic field intensity H. Its order of magnitude is $0.015/15000 = 1$ p.p.m. (part per million). Often, the one-million-fold higher $\delta \times 10^6$ is cited. With $Si(CH_3)_4$ as a reference standard, the δ's are normally negative. It has been suggested that a τ-scale, defined as

$$\tau = 10 - \frac{|\Delta|}{\nu_{\text{exp}}} 10^6,$$

should be applied in order to avoid the use of negative numbers. Since there is another advantage in doing so (to be explained), this suggestion will be followed here, also, because of its use in an important, recent monograph**.

* N. F. Ramsey, *Phys. Rev. 78*, 699 (1950); *83*, 450 (1951); *85*, 60 (1952) *86*, 243 (1952);
J. A. Pople, *Proc. Roy. Soc. A 239*, 541 (1957).
** L. M. Jackman, *Applications of Nuclear Magnetic Resonance in Organic Chemistry*, in *International Series of Monographs on Organic Chemistry* (Pergamon Press, 1959).

Now, why do we find $\tau = 9.10(9.08-9.12)$ for methyl group protons in saturated hydrocarbons, $\tau = 8.62(8.47-8.77)$ for corresponding CH_2-protons, $\tau = 2.7(2.0-3.5)$ for protons on the benzene ring, etc.?

In a uniform magnetic field, atomic and molecular electronic motions are altered so as to produce induced magnetic fields, some of which *oppose* the outer field H (diamagnetic currents) and some of which *support* it (paramagnetic currents). This complicated situation is simplified in cases where the charge distribution is axially symmetric (atoms, linear molecules). If, then, the symmetry axis of the charge distribution coincides with H (this is generally not possible all the time because of the thermal motion), only diamagnetic currents occur. In all other cases currents of both types contribute. Hence we may write

$$H_{eff} = H - D$$

relating the effective field intensity, H_{eff}, at a certain nucleus to H and a diamagnetic contribution D (which, in most cases, is a small difference between a much larger diamagnetic and a paramagnetic term). Since D is proportional to H we may write

$$H_{eff} = H(1 - \sigma)$$

where σ is the 'screening' constant.

We may now 'answer' the question about the CH_3, the CH_2, and the aromatic protons. $\tau(CH_3) > \tau(CH_2) > \tau(CH_{arom})$ 'because' the methyl group protons are magnetically the best shielded. *The better the shielding, the higher the τ-value.*

Insight into the complexity of the shielding mechanism helps in understanding, at least partially, certain experimental results which, at first glance, seem queer. Let us try, for example, to comment upon the experimental fact that $\tau(CH_4) > \tau(CH_3CH_3) > \tau(CH\equiv CH) > \tau(CH_2=CH_2)$* for the protons. Obviously, the organic chemist would have guessed another sequence.

---

* $9.7 > 9.1 > 7.8 > 4.5$ are the *approximate* τ-values.

The charge cloud surrounding protons (whether in hydrogen atoms or in molecules) has approximately spherical symmetry, irrespective of the presence of the magnetic field or chemical bonding. This situation is, of course, connected with the fact that the first electronically excited level of atomic hydrogen lies fairly high (e.g., as compared to carbon). Therefore, even if the proton is part of a molecule which incessantly changes its orientation with respect to H because of molecular rotation and vibration, mainly diamagnetic currents will flow around the proton because of the axial symmetry of the charge cloud.

This does not mean that the diamagnetic currents about *various* protons are equally strong. Even if the charge distribution is spherically symmetrical about all protons, the chemical bond to the adjoining atom may be differently polarized, i.e., the total charge remaining in the vicinity of the hydrogen may differ as a result of differences in *electronegativity* of the atom to which the hydrogen is bound. Thus, if we consider the results for CH_4 ($\tau = 9.767$), CH_3I (7.84), CH_3Br (7.32), CH_3Cl (6.95), and CH_3F (5.74), we are partially justified in interpreting the measured values in terms of electronegativity differences among the halogens.

Clearly, this is no way out of our problem above. The C–H bonds in methane, ethane, ethylene, and acetylene *do* possess different ionic character, but this character is exactly what

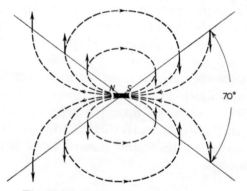

Fig. 36. Field of point magnetic dipole.

the chemist has in mind when he quotes a 'natural' sequence.

Hence, we cannot avoid considering another sort of effect, coming from the neighbouring carbon atom (or from the rest of the molecule).

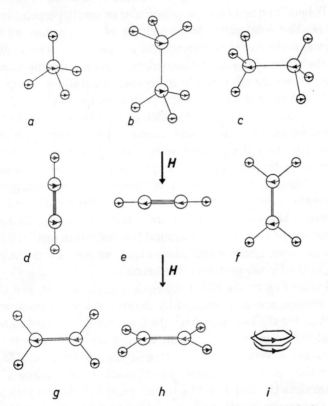

Fig. 37. Methane, ethane, acetylene, ethylene, and benzene in homogeneous magnetic field **H** directed from top to bottom of page.

Consider a proton in methane (cf. fig. 37, a). Methane has four threefold axes of symmetry. The rotating CH_4 molecule always has one C–H bond parallel or almost parallel to **H**. The molecular electronic charge cloud has almost axial symmetry about the C–H bond and, therefore, also almost axial symmetry with respect to the field direction H. As a result, only diamagnetic currents flow around the *carbon* atom. These currents exert a strong *diamagnetic* effect on the proton when it is on or close to a line through the carbon nucleus and parallel to H, whereas a weaker *paramagnetic* effect is exerted when the C–H bond in question is perpendicular or nearly perpendicular to H. The total effect is a shielding of the protons by the diamagnetic currents around the *carbon* atom. This, added to the effect of the local diamagnetic currents running around the *protons* for all possible molecular orientations, gives the observed large shielding of the protons in methane.

When *ethane* (b) is oriented with its C–C bond parallel to H, diamagnetic currents around *carbon* exert a weak *paramagnetic* effect on the protons since the C–H bonds are almost perpendicular to H. For positions (c) in which the C–C bond is perpendicular to H, carbon is encircled by paramagnetic currents acting weakly paramagnetic at the location of the protons. Making the not too unrealistic assumption that the local diamagnetic currents around the protons in methane and in ethane are about equally important, we see why the shielding of the former protons is the better one.

Proceeding to the linear molecule acetylene, it is seen that its protons are well shielded by diamagnetic currents around carbon for the case (d) where the $C{\equiv}C$ bond is parallel to H. A shielding effect is still present even if the $C{\equiv}C$ and the H direction deviate 30–35°. For positions (e) where the $C{\equiv}C$ direction is perpendicular to H, carbon is encircled by paramagnetic currents which, however, act diamagnetically at the proton location. As a result, the protons of acetylene are better shielded by magnetic effects from *carbon* than the protons of methane and ethane. But, since they are probably shielded less by their own diamagnetic currents than are the protons of ethane, because of acetylene's greater ionic character, the final result becomes $\tau(CH_3CH_3) > \tau(CH{\equiv}CH)$.

Paramagnetic currents around the carbons of ethylene exert a diamagnetic effect on the protons for certain positions of the molecule (f) and for other positions (g,h) a paramagnetic effect. Consequently, ethylenic protons are magnetically less shielded by the adjoining carbon atom than acetylenic protons. They are probably *better* shielded by local diamagnetic currents, but, in spite of this, the combined effects result in $\tau(CH_2{=}CH_2) < \tau(CH{\equiv}CH)$.

As mentioned, *aromatic* protons are still less shielded ($\tau \sim 3$). This is due to the π-electrons which cooperatively form a current loop, opposing the outer field H 'inside' the ring of the six carbons, but, of course, supporting it outside where the protons are located. Hence the low value of τ. The idea of 'ring' currents has been verified, for example, by studying compounds in which a 'bridge' of CH_2-groups runs across a benzene ring. The CH_2 protons close to the benzenoid sixfold axis were found to be highly shielded.

Figs. 36 and 37 illustrate the discussion above which aims at pointing out some of the factors governing the magnitude of measured τ-values without attempting to balance these factors even semi-quantitatively.

NMR-workers have made another important observation, namely, the existence of *spin-spin interaction*. Since spinning nuclei in the same molecule are at short distances from each other a mutual magnetic effect is to be expected beforehand. Experience has shown it to be easily observable.

Consider phosphine, PH_3. Both the protons and the phosphorus nucleus have the spin $\frac{1}{2}$. Consequently, two NMR-spectra may be observed: one, in which we 'tune in' on the P-nucleus at 25 Mc sec^{-1}, and a second at 60 Mc sec^{-1}, where we tune in on the protons, in both cases working at a field of 15 000 oersteds. The *phosphorus* resonance spectrum turns out to consist of *four* lines with the intensity ratio $1:3:3:1$. The *spacing* of the lines turns out to be independent of H. This strongly suggests that the effect is intramolecular. In harmony with this, the theory of magnetically interacting spins can account for the remaining features as well. The spinning P-nucleus experiences four possible arrangements of the spinning protons: ↑↑↑, ↑↑↓, ↑↓↓, and ↓↓↓. Hereby, the energy levels of the P-nucleus are split into four levels, and four lines arise because the selection rules forbid changes in the proton spins when the P-spin 'flips over'. The intensity relations $1:3:3:1$ follow from the fact that there is only one way of getting all three proton spins parallel to H whereas the arrangement ↑↑↓ is equivalent to the equally probable ↑↓↑ and ↓↑↑. The *proton* resonance spectrum of PH_3 consists of two lines. Since the protons are equivalent, we are dealing with their resultant spin vector $S = \Sigma_1^3 s_i$ which takes on the values $\frac{3}{2}$ and $\frac{1}{2}$. S has the components $\frac{3}{2}, \frac{1}{2}, -\frac{1}{2}$, and $-\frac{3}{2}$ along H. The corresponding energy levels are equidistant. Since transitions may take place under conditions in which the spin of the P-nucleus is either parallel or antiparallel to H, *two* lines are observed.

Spin-spin hyperfine structure is a very common phenomenon, indeed, and is more wide-spread than might be assumed at first glance. In PH_3, CH_4, $HC{\equiv}CH$, etc., the protons are truly equivalent. But take CH_3CH_2OH, ethanol. Strictly speaking, the protons of the methyl group consist of a pair of protons located symmetrically with respect to the C–C–O plane, and another proton *in* this plane. The methyl group in ethanol experimentally gives rise to three peaks, whereas interaction with the adjoining CH_2-protons ($S = 1$) would give rise to three lines from the out-of-plane CH_3-protons, and three further lines from the 'lonely' proton of the CH_3-group. Is there a reason why these two sets of lines should coincide? There is; the explanation being that the two 'kinds' of protons in the methyl group are readily exchanged because the potential barrier separating their stable positions is rather low (~ 3 kcal/mole). Therefore, the rate of exchange is so high that any proton of the methyl group experiences an average of what it would 'see' in the out-of-plane and *in*-plane positions. On the other hand, the CH_2-resonance is split into four lines because the CH_2-protons experience 4 different spin configurations of the methyl group.

A further study of spin-spin interaction may be obtained by

investigation of isotopic species such as CD_3CH_2OH. The deuteron has a magnetic moment less than one-third of the proton's. Furthermore, its spin is twice as large. Hence, spin-spin couplings are reduced by more than a factor of six when protons become substituted by deuterons. In the proton NMR-spectrum of CD_3CH_2OH, for example, the CH_2-resonance occurs as a closely spaced *septet*. The spin of the deuteron being 1 the three deuterons may attain nine different configurations ($\uparrow\uparrow\uparrow$, $\uparrow\uparrow\rightarrow$, $\uparrow\rightarrow\rightarrow$ and $\uparrow\uparrow\downarrow$, $\rightarrow\rightarrow\rightarrow$, etc.) among which seven differ energetically.

Irrespective of whether one works with a high-resolution instrument where the proton resonance of the methyl group in ethanol is seen split into components, or whether it appears unresolved, the ratio of the areas under the absorption lines for, respectively, the hydroxylic, the methylenic and the methyl protons in ethanol is predicted to be $1:2:3$, i.e., proportional to the number of protons with common chemical shift. Correctly working equipment has verified this expectation.

Anhydrous ethanol has a triple resonance for the proton of the OH-group because the protons of the adjoining CH_2-group have three spin combinations, $\uparrow\uparrow$, $\uparrow\downarrow$ and $\downarrow\downarrow$. Now, if acidified water is mixed with the ethanol, only one line is observed with a spectral position dependent on the water content. This happens because of rapid *chemical* exchange:

$$CH_3CH_2OH^* + H_3^+O \rightleftharpoons CH_3CH_2OH + H_2^+OH^*.$$

The proton, marked with an asterisk, experiences both the alcoholic and the aqueous media. All that we can measure is an average chemical shift, the position of the resonance line depending on the ethanol-water mole ratio.

VI. 4. APPLICATIONS OF NMR-SPECTRA

NMR-spectroscopy was born too late to become of great importance for the clarification of the structure of 'classical' *small* molecules. Within this area it has mainly verified what we knew, besides occasionally adding interesting features. But the NMR-studies of molecules with known structure have given the experience necessary for the work with unknowns. The clarification of the structure of di-ketene may serve as an example of the determination of a 'left-over' classical structure. The chemists were unable to decide between the formulas I–V of di-ketene:

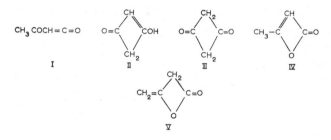

Two proton resonance lines of *equal* intensity were observed. Formula I would give two signals with intensity ratio 3:1. II would give 3 signals (1:1:2), III would give 1 signal (4 equivalent protons). IV would give two signals (3:1), V, two signals (2:2). Hence, V is to be preferred. Typically, the NMR-spectrum tells nothing about valence bond lengths and angles but it helps in choosing between a collection, such as I–V, of otherwise reasonable suggestions.

This sort of application has proved of enormous importance within the field of medium-sized and large molecules where spectroscopic and electron-diffraction technique is hard or impossible to apply. To mention a random example, *sterculic* acid was shown to have the formula

$$CH_3-(CH_2)_7-C=C-(CH_2)_7-COOH$$
$$\diagdown CH_2 \diagup$$

and *not* a formula like $CH_3-(CH_2)_7-CH^*=C=CH^*-(CH_2)_7-$ COOH, for example, because no resonance signal corresponding to ethylenic protons (H*) could be detected.

A comprehensive and authoritative treatment of several

hundred examples of application has been given by Pople, Schneider, and Bernstein*; their book starts with chapters on the theory and experimental methods of NMR-spectroscopy and should be studied by readers interested in penetrating into the subject.

Also, in a *purely analytical respect* the NMR-technique shows promise. Tables, interrelating observed chemical shifts with, for example, the type of protons involved, have been prepared**. Therefore, an observed NMR-spectrum generally serves to tell us whether an unknown compound contains aromatic, ethylenic, aldehydic (–CHO) etc. protons. Similar tables exist for other elements such as fluorine[†] and phosphorus[††]. As is seen, the information which we get in this way is an important supplement to what we can conclude from infrared (and Raman) spectra.

As already mentioned above, measurement of the areas under the CH_3-peaks, the CH_2-peaks, and the OH-peak allows a fairly accurate estimate of the *relative* number of methyl, methylenic, and hydroxylic protons $(3:2:1)$. The extension of this principle to other molecules is obvious, and it has been used with considerable success. Of course, difficulties arise in cases where the resonance signals are not separated, but merge more or less continuously. Here, the total area under all peaks is proportional to the proton concentration of the sample. Calibration may be obtained, for example, by admixing a known amount of $Si(CH_3)_4$. This non-destructive way of getting the H-content of an unknown compound already competes favourably with the 'classical' semi-micro combustion analysis.

* *High-resolution Nuclear Magnetic Resonance* (McGraw-Hill Book Co., New York and London, 1959).
** L. H. Meyer, A. Saika, and H. S. Gutowsky, *J. Am. Chem. Soc. 75*, 4567 (1953).
† H. S. Gutowsky and C. J. Hoffman, *J. Chem. Phys. 19*, 1259 (1951); N. Muller, P. C. Laüterbur, and G. F. Svatos, *J. Am. Chem. Soc. 79*, 1807 (1957).
†† H. S. Gutowsky and D. W. McCall, *J. Chem. Phys. 22*, 162 (1954).

The prospects seem even better for nuclei other than protons. Consider fluorine. All workers with fluorine compounds know the considerable analytical problems connected with quantitative determination of fluorine because of the great variety of ways (from KF to CF_4) in which fluorine combines with other elements, often to form noncombustible compounds. This host of problems seems to have found a general and common solution in the advent of the NMR-spectrograph, in cases where the problem of cost somehow has been solved.

VI. 5. INTERPRETATION OF EMR-SPECTRA

Since some nuclei and all electrons possess a spin which may 'flip over' in a magnetic field, a common treatment, as given in VI.2, is possible. So far, however, this treatment has ignored the possibility of the electron possessing an *orbital movement*, also associated with a magnetic moment.

For molecules and radicals this neglect is not serious, because the re-orientation of electronic orbits in a magnetic field is prevented by the rigidity of the nuclear framework (orbital 'quenching'). In cases of less molecular rigidity (e.g. transition-metal complexes) the 'quenching' is not absolute, resulting in fairly complicated spectra. Such spectra will not be discussed here*, where we shall confine ourselves to the case of complete 'quenching'. We shall mainly follow a recent review article by D. H. Whiffen, Quart. Rev. xii, 250 (1958).

Within the limitation indicated there is a great similarity between interpreting NMR- and EMR-hyperfine structure. Whereas the former is due to internuclear spin-spin magnetic interaction, the latter is due to interaction between nuclear and electronic spins within the same radical. If, for example, an unpaired electron gets close to one hydrogen nucleus the electron experiences the proton spin, which will be either parallel or antiparallel to *H* and, thereby, also either parallel

---

* They are treated by J. Owen and K. D. Bowers in *Rep. Progr. Phys.* *18*, 304 (1955).

or antiparallel to the electronic spin. Consequently, *two* EMR-lines of equal intensity appear. Similarly, the interaction between an electron and two *non*-equivalent protons gives rise to 4 lines of equal intensity whereas two equivalent protons – with a resultant spin of 1 – will cause 3 lines $(1:2:1)$ to appear etc. It is easily seen that if we base our reasoning on these simple laws, we have a fair chance of locating the orbitals within the radical which are occupied by an unpaired electron a fraction of the time. We shall see what takes place in the stable radical diphenylpicrylhydrazyl,

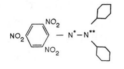

The EMR-spectrum has five lines $(1:2:3:2:1)$.

This is *not* consistent with location of the unpaired electron on N^* all the time because the nitrogen nuclear spin of 1 would split the EMR-line into a triplet $(1:1:1)$. Now, the electron might also couple to the adjoining nucleus N^{**}. Primarily, one would consider N^* and N^{**} as magnetically non-equivalent. This would mean that each of the lines predicted above would again be split in harmony with the $1:1:1$ intensity rule, i.e., we would get nine lines of equal intensity. Instead, we observe five lines. This is understandable if N^*, and N^{**} are (accidentally?) equivalent. In this case, the nitrogen nuclear spin configurations are:

$$[\uparrow\uparrow], \qquad [\uparrow\rightarrow, \rightarrow\uparrow], \qquad [\uparrow\downarrow, \downarrow\uparrow, \rightarrow\rightarrow], \qquad [\downarrow\rightarrow, \rightarrow\downarrow], \qquad [\downarrow\downarrow].$$

Therefore, the 'spin densities' on N^* and N^{**} are equal and equal 50%.

In the classical free radical $(C_6H_5)_3C^*$, triphenylmethyl, *one* line is observed possessing a very closely spaced hyperfine-structure. If the lone-pair orbital is on C^* (with no spin), this hyperfine-structure is reasonably interpreted as due to interaction with some of the aromatic protons. The assumption is brilliantly confirmed by studying $(C_6H_5)_3{}^{13}C$. The ^{13}C-nucleus has a spin of $\frac{1}{2}$, so that in the EMR-spectrum of the ^{13}C-labelled compound 2 equally strong, well-separated lines (with hyperfine structure) appear.

If the radical ion $(C_6H_5)_3N^+$ is studied, *one* line with very narrow fine-structure is again observed. Since the magnetic moment of ^{14}N is about two-thirds that of ^{13}C, and since its spin is 1 as compared to carbon's $\frac{1}{2}$, the coupling with the electron spin would be less by a factor of $\frac{1}{3}$, everything else being equal. Actually, a far smaller coupling is observed. This can be interpreted as meaning that the electronegative nitrogen atom cannot have a large charge deficit. It attracts charge from the phenyl rings so that the unpaired electron is 'smeared out' all over the three rings. At each of the 18 ring-carbons there is an (average) spin-density of a few percent.

In the examples mentioned above the structure of the radical was known. In many cases, analysis of an observed hyperfine structure helps to prove what free radical is present. By the action of X-rays on $Zn(CH_3)_2$ at $77°K$, a free radical is produced, giving rise to 4 lines $(1:3:3:1)$. This speaks strongly in favour of assuming that the radical is CH_3. Here, the protons would actually give rise to 4 lines $(1:3:3:1)$ when coupling with an unpaired electron.

VI. 6. APPLICATIONS OF EMR-SPECTRA

First of all, EMR-spectroscopy has provided us with a long-needed tool for easily and unambiguously showing the presence and estimating the amounts of free radicals, even in rather small concentrations. A fresh impression of the complexity of nature has hereby been obtained. Somewhat unexpectedly, perhaps, free radicals are found almost everywhere, perhaps due to stray radiation of high energy. Free radicals may easily be formed in almost any material by irradiation with γ-rays, X-rays, etc. Since they may be stable for days, 'radiation damage' is a matter of great importance. A quantitative estimate of the free radical concentration is not hard to obtain because the integrated area under an EMR-line is proportional to the electron spin concentration, irrespective of the chemical surroundings. Each type of equipment is conveniently calibrated by recording, for example, the EMR-spectrum of a known amount of diphenylpicrylhydrazyl.

Secondly, interpretation of resolved hyperfine structure may tell us which radical is present. At the same time the distribution of the 'odd' electron inside the radical may be inferred. In proportion to the fast growing interest in free radicals as such, EMR-spectroscopy will be of increasing importance to chemistry and physics.

TABLE OF PHYSICAL CONSTANTS FREQUENTLY USED IN MOLECULAR SPECTROSCOPY

Velocity of light in empty space, c.	$c = 2.99793 \times 10^{10}$ cm sec^{-1}
Planck's constant, h.	$h = 6.62517 \times 10^{-27}$ erg sec
Avogadro's number, N	
Referred to chemical atomic weight scale:	$N = 6.02320 \times 10^{23}$
Referred to physical atomic weight scale:	$N = 6.02486 \times 10^{23}$
Boltzmann's constant, k.	$k = 1.38044 \times 10^{-16}$ erg deg^{-1}
Electronic mass, μ.	$\mu = 9.1083 \times 10^{-28}$ gram
Electronic charge, e.	$e = 4.80286 \times 10^{-10}$ abs.e.s.u.
Gas constant, R.	$R = 1.9878$ cal deg^{-1} mole^{-1}

INDEX